NO EARTHLY COMMAND

And whosoever will be chief among you, let him be your servant

Their bodies are buried in peace but their name liveth for evermore;
The people will tell of their wisdom and the congregation will show forth their praise

No Earthly Command

Being an enquiry into the life of
Vice-Admiral the Reverend Alexander Riall Wadham Woods
D.S.O. *and bar*
of whom it was said that during the Battle of Jutland
while Signals Officer to
the Admiral of the Grand Fleet, Sir John Jellicoe
he received an 'interposed message'
telling him to serve God

by

ARTHUR CALDER-MARSHALL

RUPERT HART-DAVIS
36 *Soho Square* **London** W1
1957

PRINTED IN GREAT BRITAIN
BY EBENEZER BAYLIS AND SON, LTD., THE
TRINITY PRESS, WORCESTER, AND LONDON

To Margaret

FOREWORD

I WISH to thank all those who have helped me in writing this book. The love which this good man bore to and inspired in others was extended to me, his unworthy biographer, in ways which I did not believe possible. To enumerate the many hundreds who have helped would be tedious if confined to a mere list; yet to attempt to specify exactly how I benefited from each individual is beyond my powers. I know only that without them as a whole, the task would have been accomplished even less ably than it has been.

I feel that I owe to some of them an apology, because in writing or talking to them, I conveyed the impression that I intended a full-dress portrait of the admiral and priest, a conventional biography. In the pages which follow, it will be plain how and why the project of a Life became an Enquiry.

Apart from these individual assistants and collaborators, I wish to thank The Lords Commissioners of the Admiralty for their permission to study certain of their documents; to Messrs Cassells for permission to quote from Admiral Sir Reginald Bacon's *The Life of John Rushworth, Earl Jellicoe* and to the Student Christian Movement for permission to quote from Dr Olive Wyon's *The School of Prayer*.

Arthur Calder-Marshall

Cranleigh, Surrey

PART ONE

CHAPTER ONE

In July 1955 I was sitting in the garden of the house I had just bought, when I was called to the telephone. As I went in to answer it, I prayed it would be a job. Five beautiful months of spring and summer had been wasted house-hunting. During that time I had been unable to tackle anything more ambitious than short stories and broadcasts. Now I wanted something bigger to keep me busy.

"Mr Calder-Marshall?" I recognized the voice of Jo, the switchboard operator at Rupert Hart-Davis. "Mr Milton Waldman wants you."

Milton's voice came on the line, asking the usual questions, was I very busy?

"What is it?" I asked. I rather distrusted Milton's enthusiasm since he had suggested that I should go to live in Malaga to write the life of an Indian lion-tamer.

"Are you coming to London?" he asked.

"I could," I said. "But I'd like to know what it's about first."

"Well, it's not easy to explain over the phone," he said. "But I've had a guy called Boston in my office—he's just left—and the idea seems crazy to me. But if he's right, there's a lot of money in this. At any rate he's got a letter from Ultramontane Films Inc. offering him five thousand dollars for an option on the film rights, if there's a hard-cover book."

"What's the hard-cover book to be about?"

"It seems there was a Vice-Admiral Woods, who was

Signals Officer to Jellicoe on the *Iron Duke* during the Battle of Jutland and he got a signal from the Almighty to serve Him and so he went and became a priest down in the East End."

"Was it in cipher or *en clair*?" I asked.

"All this guy had was an obituary notice from the *New York Times*," said Milton. "It didn't say. I've got the clipping in the office and I'd like you to see it."

"Tell me, Milton. Do you believe in all his?"

"I believe in the letter from Ultramontane Films Inc. That's genuine enough."

This is the cutting which Milton showed me next morning.

CALL FROM "NO EARTHLY CAPTAIN"

REV. A. R. WOODS, BRITISH EX-ADMIRAL DIES

A former British Rear-Admiral who ended a brilliant naval career because of a command from "no earthly captain" died today at the age of 74, a poor man's parson in London's shabby East End.

Few members of the impoverished congregation knew that the Rev. Alexander Riall Woods had been a high-ranking hero of the Battle of Jutland in 1916 and that he was the son of an admiral.

Nor did they know his story of a divine revelation during that World War I action, which changed the course of his life.

To them Mr Woods was known as the "shy parson" because he never talked about his personal life and background. He devoted his time to the "down and outs" in the sprawling dockland area and they loved him for it.

Mr Woods preached at St Paul's, Whitechapel, known as the "Dockland Church" and became chaplain to a near-by seamen's home. Everybody knew that the parson understood sailors and the sea. His weather-beaten face and steady eyes spoke of first-hand experience at sea and many concluded he had been a deckhand in his youth.

The congregation had planned this week to celebrate his twenty-one years at their church. Old-timers recalled how as a newcomer he preached his first sermon there to a congregation of seven compared with the overflowing audiences after he had won their hearts.

For twenty-one years Mr Woods lived under the same rough conditions as his parishioners. He did not once look back at the aristocratic life he had led as a Royal Naval Officer.

Until the Battle of Jutland Mr Woods had devoted his career to the Navy in the tradition of his family. At the height of that battle he underwent a mystic experience.

As a Captain he was in charge of signal operations for the British fleet against the Germans. In the midst of giving signals he received what he called "an interposed signal which came from no earthly captain but from a higher command". Although awe-stricken, he recovered himself in time to conduct the signal operations through the battle. He received the Distinguished Service Order for his heroism under fire.

For fifteen years until he had served his time, Mr Woods remained in the Navy but wondered about that strange signal. In 1931 the 51-year-old admiral declined a further appointment and entered a theological college. Two years later he was ordained as a minister of the Church of England. He asked for and got the East End assignment.

Five years after his retirement Mr Woods was raised to the rank of Vice-Admiral. Since 1933 he has been chaplain of the Red Ensign Club, and assistant curate of St Paul's, Whitechapel.

"What do you think of it?" Milton asked.

"It's an obvious lie," I said. "If Woods received an 'interposed message'—whatever that means—from God in 1916, why did he wait all those years to obey it? It doesn't make sense."

"And yet an obituary from the *New York Times*."

"Who put it out? B.U.P.?"

"No. Reuter's. There must be something in it."

"Woods quite obviously *did* leave the Navy and become a priest—not just a cosy priest, but down in the

London docks. That's what interests me, not this interposed message."

"All I want is so you'll meet Boston and go down and
see for yourself. And if you say there's a story, we're
interested. But otherwise not."

Boston came down to visit me on his way to Goodwood
races. He was interested in a film about, as far as I could
gather, a small boy who made a fortune out of a sextuple
bet. I liked him. He was a quiet Californian who spoke
softly about huge sums of money. Usually people
raise their voices about money when it gets into five
figures.

I asked how he had stumbled on this fortune and he told
me that he had read the obituary notice at breakfast in
New York and it had come to him as an inspiration that it
was just the subject which Pieter Paulus needed as a
follow-up to the film he had made on a parish priest,
entitled *Suffer Little Children*. "People don't want Sex
any more," he said, "they want God. *Suffer Little Children*
was the biggest box-office success in the history of Ultramontane Films." He drew out his pocket book and
showed me his copy of the obituary notice and the letter
he had received from Pieter Paulus. He handled them
with as much reverence as if they were First Folios of
Shakespeare. "You writers don't seem to know it,"
he said, "but that's where the money is. Look at Billy
Graham."

I did not want to look at Billy Graham. I tried to tell
the truth. It had never brought me a fortune, but I
hadn't starved.

"Of course the first thing we've got to fix is the releases,"
he said. "That's my job, but you might as well come
down to see the General—that's the Admiral's brother,
who's acting for the family. Then there's a niece called
Lettice. She's secretary to a clergyman in Mayfair. And

of course the Admiralty, they're being very unco-opera-tive."

I knew that the "releases" were documents which film companies prepared to guarantee themselves against legal action by any people portrayed in a "real-life" film. They are horrifying documents and I could understand anybody faced with them not being very co-operative. "But how do the Admiralty come in?" I asked.

"Perhaps it isn't the Admiralty exactly," Boston an-swered. "But there's a fleet of Admirals on the committee of the Sailors' Home and Red Ensign Club—that's the place in Whitechapel where the old boy was Chaplain. They won't sign, though I've offered them a cut for the Club. They're not movie-minded and they just can't see what a power of good a film might do for them. All they keep saying is, 'How can we be sure they won't cast Errol Flynn as the Padre? Will you guarantee that?' And of course I can't. You know what movies are."

I did and I felt that the Admirals must have a pretty good idea too. "But why have you got to have releases from the Sailors' Home?" I asked. "What's it got to do with them, really?"

"I thought if you went down to talk to them, it might make a difference. I scare the pants off them, because I'm American."

It was soon time for him to go. We fixed to drive down to East Bergholt the next day to see General Woods. "And remember," he said, as he got into his hired car, "there's big money in this."

During the drive from London to Suffolk next day, he kept recurring to the big money, the syndication rights, the digest rights, the paper-back rights. He spoke with a quiet excitement and at times almost religious awe of the money which would come pouring in on us, though he became vague when I tried to determine the proportions in which this fortune was to be allocated. He had promised money to the family, to the Sailors' Home, to St Paul's Church for Seamen in the Port of London. Then his own expenses had been heavy. "I think that if I write the book, I should receive some payment too," I said.

"But of course," he answered, "but of course."

We talked of films and film-makers, discovering that we had mutual friends and acquaintances, in assessment of whom we agreed. Apart from dollar preoccupation, which was a national rather than personal characteristic, he was a sensitive, imaginative man; and also, I discovered, a rather frightened one. He had had a thrombosis, which had undermined his confidence in living. He seemed to keep catching sight of death out of the tail of his eye; I suspected this film was more than just a moneyspinner for him. He wanted it to do good.

We got on better with one another than with finding the way to Hill House, East Bergholt. We covered most of the Constable country before we arrived at the General's house. "Only it turns out that he's only a Brigadier," Boston said. "Not that it matters for the film, I suppose."

We were three-quarters of an hour late for luncheon, but Brigadier-General Woods was unperturbed. He was a small, upright, grey-haired man in his seventies, with bright alert eyes, a longish nose and a mouth which turned down at the ends when he smiled. Though not taciturn, he gave the impression of saying only a small part of what he could say if he chose; a man whose reticence covered great spiritual reserves.

His wife, who possessed the peculiar name of Eucharis, was ten to fifteen years younger. In temperament she was his opposite, a bubbly woman, full of laughter and friendliness, who clearly often said things which she subsequently regretted. She chattered not out of malice but out of a childlike innocence or the desire to have no secrets. "You'll get more out of her than out of him,"

Boston had warned me, "but what you do get out of him will probably be more worthwhile."

There was also their son Guy, a handsome young Marine officer, on leave from Malta, very jolly and open-seeming, but more taking after his father, I realized, when Boston made what to him was an embarrassing remark. "Your grandfather was in the Navy. So were your Uncle Alex and Uncle Arthur. Your father and your Uncle Charles were in the Army. And now you in the Marines. To what would you attribute this tradition of public service?"

Guy Woods was nonplussed for a moment. Then he said, "I suppose it's because we're all too lazy to earn a living in Civvy Street."

I liked that answer and so did Boston. As he said later. "That's your British upper middle class. Amazing aren't they?"

Though we had arrived late, the leg of lamb cooked by Eucharis Woods was not overdone. As we ate, we talked over aspects of this film project.

"I can't imagine what poor Alex would say at the idea of a film about his life," Mrs Woods said.

"I can," said the Brigadier-General. " 'Why pick on me?' That's what he'd say. And I must say, I echo the sentiment."

"What are you going to make a film *about*?" Guy asked. "He was just a very holy man. But you can't make a film about that."

I saw Boston's hand go towards his pocket book. He wanted to touch the cutting from the *New York Times*, that alchemical slip of paper. "What about the message at Jutland?"

"There was no message," the Brigadier-General said; "it was all a newspaper story."

"Alex was furious," Mrs Woods said. "This news-paper reporter woman went down to the East End, just after he was ordained. She wanted to 'get his story', isn't that what they call it? Of course, Alex wouldn't talk . . ."

"Hated the Press," interjected her husband. "Can't say I blame him."

"But this woman was so persistent that Alex gave her the address of his sister, Edyth. Just to get rid of her, you see. And it was from Edyth this reporter woman said she got the story. Apparently she went along and said, 'Your brother wants you to tell me everything.'"

The Brigadier-General saw me opening my mouth and anticipated me. "You can't ask Edyth, because she's dead. Died during the war."

Boston looked uncomfortable. "I know these things get sensationalized. But there must be a germ of truth even behind the wildest story."

"Of course, Alex was always very reticent," Mrs Woods said. "He never spoke about himself, did he, Hugh?"

"Why should he?" asked the Brigadier-General.

"Did he suddenly become religious?" I asked. "After the Battle of Jutland?"

"No, he was always religious, right from the beginning. We all were. As a family, Father was and Mother was; and all of us."

"But not High," his wife said. "The family was Low. But of course Alex became very High. And so did Charles and Dorothy—that's the eldest brother and his wife."

"And when did he become High?" I asked, thinking that this might be the germ of the Jutland story.

"I don't know," said the Brigadier-General. "I think it was the chaplain on the training ship *Britannia*. But I can't really say. You see with two of us in the Army and two in the Navy, we saw very little of one another after we were boys. I'm afraid there's almost nothing I can give you."

"Of course I can tell you something," Mrs Woods said, "because I knew him from a girl."

"But that was later," said her husband.

"Yes, of course," she agreed. "It was much later. When was Alex born?"

"Eighteen-eighty," said the Brigadier-General, "the last of six."

"Of course the father, Inspector-General Woods, had a most awfully interesting life. He was Queen Victoria's surgeon on the Royal Yacht."

"And of course he used to go to Balmoral, too. He was a great favourite of the Queen."

"And Alex, you know, got his name from Queen Alexandra, or the Princess of Wales, as she then was. She was his godmother!"

"No," said the Brigadier-General. "She was upset that my father didn't ask her, she said. She would like to have been."

"And the family tradition goes that when she saw all the Woods children together, she said that she had never seen such a handsome family in all her life."

"Family tradition is not always trustworthy," said her husband.

I saw a ray of hope. "There must be family papers, then, about that period." That could be fascinating, a stethoscopic view of Queen Victoria and her enormous family, the beat of princely pulses and the inflammation of royal tonsils.

"There were stacks of them, when Father died," Hugh said. "But Charles and Arthur, being the executors, destroyed the lot. I was furious."

"But there must be diaries, or log-books," Boston said.

"There would be log-books in the Admiralty, when he was Captain—though I doubt if they'd tell you anything. And he didn't keep any journals that I know."

"He wasn't a writing man," Eucharis Woods said. "He seldom wrote a letter. Picture postcards mostly. Of churches."

"Or ships," said her husband.

"Or ships' chapels. That was the best of all."

Before we left, the Brigadier-General took me on one side. "I want you to advise me about this question of releases. Have you seen them? They scare me out of my wits."

"Anything to do with film company legal contracts is always scarifying," I answered. "One feels so insulted at being treated as if one is a crook. But they've had so many crooks to deal with you can't blame them."

"I don't like signing a document like that," he said. "But if you say it is all right . . . you know more about these things."

"I can't advise you," I said, "not at the moment. I am primarily interested in a book on your brother, a book worth writing. If there is no material I shall report that to Hart-Davis and that's the end of it, as far as we are concerned. But if there is a book, it can't be written without that money for the film option, because there's no written material to work from. It means months of research."

"Boston keeps pestering us to sign. What shall we do?"

"The sort of film it is depends on the sort of book. The book depends on who writes it. If I were you, I wouldn't sign until I knew who was going to write the book. If I feel I'm not the person to write it, I'll tell you who would do it well. I promise you that."

"Well," said Boston as we drove back, past the church of East Bergholt. "I think we've made some progress. Of course, they are still worried about those releases."

"Wouldn't you be?"

"Of course I should." He laughed. "But of course one has to take a risk."

"We don't," I said. "They do."

We went on talking, but I was thinking about Hugh, Eucharis and Guy Woods in that mellow, shabby, early Victorian house on the hill, their obvious differences in character and the love which united them in a quiet, contagious happiness.

"I think you quieted their suspicions," Boston said. "They don't know quite what to make of me because I'm American."

"That's what I'm afraid of," I said. "So let's get this clear. I'm not going to be committed to this book, just because the Woods are nice people. I said I didn't think there was a book; and I still don't think there's a book. I want to see Lettice Woods and go down to the Sailors' Home."

"I was going to suggest that," he said. "And the Vicar of the church, Father Williamson. We'll go down to the East End together. But it would be better if you saw Lettice alone."

"Because you're an American?"

He laughed. "Let's say, yours is a fresh face."

Later he said, "By the way, Tony Veiller asked to be reminded to you."

"I haven't seen Tony in years," I said. "Not since the War. We worked together for a fortnight on a one-and-a-half-reeler which either of us could have written in a couple of days. But that didn't suit Anatole Litvak. It had to be two people for two weeks, or it couldn't be good. 'I want this *literate*,' he kept saying, when we asked him what was wrong."

"Dear Colonel Litvak! I served under him too," Boston said. "But anyway, Tony was very nice about you. You know I was going to get an American writer, Paul Gallico or someone; but I thought better of it. I asked Tony what English writer I ought to get and he suggested you."

"I thought the suggestion came from Milton," I said.

"That was the curious thing," he answered. "I went along to Hart-Davis's, not to talk writers; just to sell the hard-cover book. And then Milton said they'd only do it if you wrote it. Quite a coincidence!"

"It is," I agreed, "when you remember that there are over eight thousand authors in Great Britain."

"So you see you're the man for the job," he said.

"What I am not convinced is that there is any job," I answered.

CHAPTER TWO

Boston had not come over to London merely to secure
releases and get a contract for the Woods book, of which
he knew nothing more than it ought to be called *No
Earthly Command*. He had other larger fish to fry. It was
about a week before we went down to the Sailors' Home.
I did not see Lettice Woods in the meantime. I should
know better what questions to ask her, when I had seen
how and where her uncle had lived.

"Give me some idea of the set-up," I said to Boston
as we drove down through the City towards the East End.

"I wouldn't know," he said. "If this were the States,
I could tell you. But I don't understand your quaint old
English ways. This club is for merchant seamen, not the
Royal Navy; and there's big shipping company money
behind it. My hunch is that they're scared the film will
show up living conditions. It's pretty tough now, and
during the depression it must have been terrible."

"It was," I said. "I remember the time when police-
men had to go down Cable Street in pairs. Just about
the time Woods went there."

"The manager of the place is a guy called Stride—
'Boy Stride' the old Padre used to call him. I don't
know if you can make him talk. He seems to be afraid
of this committee, the admirals and the shipping men.
Spent all his life in the club, since he was a boy, you
know, and it's more than his job's worth to do anything
on his own. That's my view."

We had passed through the City of London, the dark-suited men with the rolled umbrellas, the bright office girls, the gravity of business. On the right was the Tower of London, as always an astonishing building to find still standing in this modern city. Running north and south the light and heavy traffic of East England was trickling across Tower Bridge. Beyond was Dockland.

The walls of the City of London have been razed, but there is still a perceptible barrier marking the City limits. Behind us were the clerks and the cashiers, the managers and their secretaries, coming from homes in the south, the west and north; and immediately we had crossed the stream of the Tower Bridge traffic we were in a different world, the world of seamen, warehousemen, dockers, night-watchmen and those who cater for their needs.

Some ports are exciting. Their violence and excesses, which are natural wherever men are confronted with the difficulties of a lonely leisure, are mitigated by sunshine and bright colours. But the Port of London is not one of these. The river itself is beautiful, no longer silver Thames but dark as dirt, yet always lovely because of its restless ebb and flow and the continual, various traffic of craft under the ever-changing light.

I once lived in a converted cinnamon wharf, a narrow, deep house on the Thames at Rotherhithe. There was never a moment when it was not beautiful. At high tide when the level of the river was a foot above the kitchen floor and at low when the broken bottles and rusting pram-wheels were revealed upon the mud; in fog when Tower Bridge and Wapping Old Stairs vanished from sight and ships passed like ghosts, the sad air shaken with the boom of foghorns; in milky sunshine and the cold splendour of rain racing up or down the reaches. Dawn and sunset, midnight and high noon, always the same and always different, as a perfect wife or husband, the brown Thames was magnificent.

But between Tower Bridge and Greenwich there are scarcely half a dozen places the river can be seen from. The people of Bermondsey and Rotherhithe, of Stepney, Shadwell, Ratcliffe and Wapping are cut off from this one open space where the spirit can expand, by the high, smoke-black walls of wharfs and warehouses. The East End is like an enormous prison, enclosed on the landward sides by distance, the miles of mean similar streets a barrier to escape as effective as barbed wire. What surprises me is not that some people choose alcohol as the nearest way out, but that more don't.

The Ensign Street entrance to the Sailors' Home and Red Ensign Club was only a couple of minutes' drive from Tower Bridge, a tall building in the institutional manner, towering above the low terrace of houses on the opposite side of the narrow street. A group of West Indian or African sailors were standing outside a brightly painted café, engaged in what might be friendly badinage or the beginning of a brawl, one of those unpredictable eddies in idleness.

We went up steps to the door of the Home. It puzzled me until I realized that it was an old building which had been made over. It had a partially new façade, a new look to the hall and the restaurant on the right. But it did not quite convince, because it was the back of the building. The main entrance was in Dock Street, running parallel to Ensign Street. But the old block in Dock Street had been pulled down and a vast new edifice was rising in its place.

The Ensign Street entrance was complicated. On the left just inside the door was a little room on the door of which was painted WELFARE OFFICER. Then there was a tiny porter's office and beyond that a reception desk and cashier's office all in one.

A man, who looked rather like a small edition of T. S. Eliot in his poet's uniform "dressed like a bankclerk", was talking to a portly seaman, a Danish ship's cook as I found later.

"That's Stride," Boston whispered, as the small Eliot broke off and turned towards us.

Boston introduced me and Stride asked us into his office, which lay hidden away behind the reception desk. "What can I do for you gentlemen?" he asked in a voice that was very soft. It wasn't what bad novelists call "silky". It was more like *crêpe de Chine*. He had a feline personality.

And suddenly Boston, whom I had labelled as a "smooth operator", became very canine. I won't say that it was nothing to do with what we had come to discuss; but it was very little. They were as different as cat and dog and in a moment there was going to be a squabble which would have nothing to do with the Padre.

"I know that you can't tell me anything about the Padre without the consent of the committee, Mr Stride," I said. "All I wanted to know was whether I could see the chapel and where the Padre worked and slept."

Stride shrugged his shoulders and pulled down the ends of his mouth. "It's my lords and masters. You can understand. There was a very unfortunate feature on the B.B.C. Television. They didn't like it."

"I think that Mr Boston would probably prefer to stay here. He hasn't been very well. Perhaps a cup of tea . . ."

"Or an iced Coca Cola," Boston suggested.

"A cup of tea," said Stride firmly and he went out to give the order, asking me to follow him.

We left the modernized section and came into a fiercely institutional region, clean and hard-wearing but utterly without taste or eye for beauty, the sort of place which serves for police-court cases, but which as a home for people is only good enough for good works.*

* This was the central block, which the Committee had hoped to rebuild, but had been forced to leave as it was, owing to lack of funds.

I felt depressed by the darkness, the durability and the sensible paint. "We have kept the Padre's rooms just as they were," said Stride. "But the question is, where are the keys?"

He left me waiting in an enlargement of a passage-way in which were an old sofa, some chairs and tables and a bookcase containing a number of well-worn volumes. I went over to see if there was any plan behind the selection of titles, whether this was a live library or one of those Old Books Homes, in which decrepit volumes pass the evening of their days before making that last sad journey in a sack to Salvage.

I now saw that the passage-way had originally been part of a very large room, the whole east side of which had been cut off to make a chapel and the north-west corner to provide the Padre's accommodation.

Stride had now returned, having solved the problem of entering the Padre's rooms by some means which was not clear but was still worrying him. On a deeper level of anxiety he was fussing about the film and whether he ought to give me any information, partly because of the television film which had been made about the club and partly because the Padre was not the sort of person to appear in a film. I thought, 'I'll never get any stuff out of this chap.'

We went into a small dark cubicle. "This is where the Padre slept," Stride said, "after he fell and broke his femur, that is. He used to be over in the Dock Street building, which they're rebuilding. But then he had to be near the chapel. This is as he left it."

In one corner of the cubicle was a high truckle bed, made up with coarse army blankets. Over in the opposite corner a pair of leg-irons attached to heavy army boots, terrific things with pads and straps going right up to the hips. "Did he always have those?" I asked.

"After his accident," Stride said; "before that they

27

were only up to the knee. The progressive muscular atrophy was well advanced when he came here in the 'thirties."

I touched them, trying to overcome my repugnance to these surgical aids by remembering that to those who have to wear them they are a blessing and the disease a curse. "Could he move with them?" I asked.

"He couldn't move without. William, the steward who looked after him, had to take them off when he was in bed and put them on before he could get up. You must meet William. His real name is Lewis, but the Padre loved Richmal Crompton's William books and gave him the nickname."

I looked round this sombre little cell with a feeling not merely of depression but also of distaste. Austerity I had been prepared for; but such ugliness, such drabness was surely unnecessary. Stride said: "He didn't trouble about comfort."

We went into the second cubicle leading off the first. It was shabby, untidy, cluttered with junk, a few battered old books, including a run of Richmal Crompton, a coloured reproduction of a photograph of Queen Elizabeth II, a signed photograph of Admiral Jellicoe, a photograph of the *Iron Duke*, snapshots of people and some reproductions of the poorest quality of the most sentimental religious pictures. It was if anything more depressing than the bedroom, which had expressed only indifference to surroundings. This study vividly demonstrated a personality, patriotic, loyal, friendly, God-loving, but devoid of taste and intellectual curiosity. Woods had not been my sort of person.

Stride caught my feeling of disappointment. He could see that I was evolving reasons why I shouldn't explore this sad little province of misguided devotion. This upset him. It was easy enough for him to oppose a book on the Padre which might be made into a film, so long as someone wanted to write the book. But Stride had such a devotion to the Padre that it was intolerable that a writer should reject the subject as dull. I could sense him steaming himself up. To avoid an outbreak, I peered at a little photograph, about one inch square, stuck in the corner of one of the picture-frames. It was a portrait of the head and shoulders of a young girl, who was certainly very pretty and perhaps beautiful. "Who is that?" I asked. I looked more closely; it was not prettiness or beauty that made that young face remarkable, but something else. Exactly what it was eluded me, but all I knew was that I wanted to meet her.

"Oh, that's his Margaret," Stride said, "Margaret Earler."

"D'you think I could see her?" I asked.

"I don't know," he said. "She got out of bed to come to his funeral; and she had a relapse. T.B., you know. She's very ill and it distresses her to speak about the Padre."

We went across the passage into the chapel. It was a plain, quiet place, the sort of chapel one would find on board ship. I discovered later that it was modelled on the chapel aboard the *Iron Duke*. It was very trim, with shining brass candlesticks and a fine altar-cloth. With one exception the pictures were awful from an æsthetic point of view. The exception was a lovely Madonna and Child. I wondered if the Padre had really a taste in art which he was prepared to violate because he saw religious art as a means to an end and most people responded to the obvious and sentimental more easily than to the restrained and beautiful. I decided it was unlikely; taste would have betrayed itself somehow in his own two rooms.

"After his accident, when he couldn't say Holy Communion, it nearly broke his heart," said Stride. "He couldn't stand, you see."

I couldn't see why not being able to stand should have prevented his celebrating; nor could I see why not being able to celebrate should break anyone's heart, when God knew it was an impossibility. Yet obviously from Stride's voice it was true.

We went back into the passage and sat down. Stride began to talk about the dead man. He was certain that there had been no revelation at Jutland. The Padre did not believe in violent conversions. His was no road to Damascus. The "overflowing congregations" described in the obituary notice were the invention of the journalist. The number of the faithful had remained very small. Yet without his realizing it the Padre had established himself in the hearts of the people. "At his funeral," Stride said, "the church was packed and outside there were on the pavements Jews and Christians, whites and coloureds, hundreds of them, and the police had to come along to get the traffic down Dock Street. And they kept saying that he was a saint, though very few of them had been near the church in his lifetime. And of course it's true. He *was* a saint."

I did not find that hard to believe. No man could have chosen the Sailors' Home and lived there all those years in those conditions unless he was a saint. "But how did they know him, if they didn't come to the church?"

"You should have seen him during the war," Stride said. "Out night after night in the blitz, going from shelter to shelter—he wore a tin helmet, but only as a good example. He believed God would not take him unless He willed. And with those legs it was amazing the ground he covered. That's how everybody knew him."

We talked for a long time, secure in the knowledge that Boston was too afraid of his heart to climb the stairs after us, and Stride, the man who had begun by disapproving of a film because it could only be a travesty of the simple, unspectacular life of the Padre, convinced me that there certainly could be a book, and perhaps even an honest film, about this Vice-Admiral with the crippled legs who had come down to the East End and in his devotion to his God grown oblivious to his own physical suffering.

There are some subjects which demand to be written because they are so obviously dramatic, stories like that of a Signals Officer who in the middle of a battle receives an interposed message from God. This did not seem to me to be such a story. It was far more intriguing, the story of a man who had behaved in a way which was incomprehensible to me and yet whose holiness and sincerity were beyond doubt. I was almost glad that he lacked any distinction of taste or intellect, because it would limit me to the study of goodness and holiness.

I began to probe Stride about the sources I could tap for the Padre's life. Tantalizingly he started to retreat once more, the servant of a committee who might forbid him to co-operate and the friend of the Padre who would have flinched from the idea of becoming the subject of a book. Stride, I imagine, was as uncertain about the book as I was, but for different reasons. We both wanted to think it over.

"What did you make of Stride?" Boston asked in the car.

"It's part of his strength to appear soft," I said. "When he comes to an obstacle, he goes round it."

"I mean the releases," Boston said. "Will he co-operate?"

I wasn't very interested in the releases, except to prevent Boston scaring everybody concerned by presenting them with those horrifying documents and promising untold dollars if they signed.

"We must go and see Father Williamson while we're down here," Boston said. "He undertook to sign the Admiralty up and now he's renegued."

We stopped outside a decent-sized house in Dock Street, which appeared small because it stood between

St Paul's Church for Seamen and the steel skeleton of the
new Sailors' Home and Red Ensign Club building. "I
never thought the Church would let me down," Boston
said sadly.

We were shown into the Vicar's study and told that
Father Williamson would be with us in a moment. I
looked round the room. There was more evidence of
learning here than in the Padre's study in the Sailors'
Home, a full bookcase running the length of the wall,
containing mostly theological works. "Williamson was an
East End boy who made good," Boston said. "A dramatic
personality."

At that moment the door opened and a cassocked
figure swept in with hand outstretched. "My dear chap,
this is a pleasure. How lucky I happened to be in."

The Reverend Joseph Williamson was a grey-haired,
handsome and vigorous man in his sixties. He had an
intense but limited concentration. His wife had told him
that Boston was there to see him and he greeted him with
such warmth and cordiality that he did not notice that
anybody else was in the room until Boston introduced me
as "the writer". Williamson then turned to me and shook
me by the hand with equal warmth. It was as if his
attention was beamed like a torch; it shone brightly in
one direction or another, but not all round. While he
talked to me, he appeared oblivious of Boston. He wore
spectacles and I thought it possible that he was short-
sighted and in consequence had a limited field of vision.
I never found out whether this was correct, though I was
to discover later that he suffered from a form of mental
myopia.

At the moment, however, I was too concerned with
disclaiming being "the writer" to analyse our host. "At
the moment I'm only an investigator," I said, "and I don't
see what there is to write a book about. There was no
miracle at Jutland. We're all agreed on that."

"You haven't talked to Lettice?" said Father William-son. "She asked the Padre and he said, 'Well, it was no earthly command.' That sounds as though there was something."

I had agreed with Boston when he had said that at the core of every newspaper story there must be a germ of truth. I could not conceive the possibility of a journalist, however unscrupulous, making up a story without a thread of fact. "I've been wondering," I said, "whether Woods, hearing guns fired in anger for the first time in his naval career, suddenly realized what the whole thing was about. I mean, the losses . . . they came through to him, and him first. It might have been that it was a sort of revelation that he was in the wrong service. He should have been saving souls, not killing bodies."

I was using Father Williamson as a sounding-board. I could imagine myself, if I had ever come to occupy a position in the Royal Navy before 1914—sports, smartness and the amenities of naval stations—suddenly being apalled by the carnage of a naval battle and becoming a militant, instead of a conforming, Christian.

"It's a possibility," Father Williamson said. "One can imagine that happening." He went over to his bookcase and after a brief search came back with a copy of his Church Magazine. "You ought to see this," he said.

While Boston pursued his grievance with Father Williamson, I glanced at the magazine. On the cover was printed:

The Pilot
ST PAUL'S CHURCH of the Port of London for Seamen
Memorial Number to
Vice-Admiral the Rev.
ALEXANDER RIALL WADHAM WOODS, D.S.O.,
Who Died on All Saints' Day, 1954

Beneath was a photograph of the Vice-Admiral in full-dress uniform with the gold braid and all the medals up. His face was like his brother's, the Brigadier-General's. His nose was if anything longer and thinner. The nostrils arched a little higher, the lines were repeated in the arch of the hooded eyelids and the mouth curved down at the corners.

I had always believed—since at the age of eight I had read an article in *Home Notes* on the choice of a husband —that a man whose mouth curved down at the ends was of a melancholy temperament and so to be avoided as a husband. I had long since revised my opinion about the advice. Many women prefer melancholy husbands. Some sparkling wives, for example, need the setting of a lugubrious mate. But I had accepted the equation of a down-turned mouth with melancholy.

The Vice-Admiral's mouth exploded the fallacy. The mouth and eyes were intensely amused in a very quiet, perceptive way. He was a man who could appreciate a joke without guffawing. It would not need to be shared to be enjoyed. Yet a glance from those twinkling eyes could transmit it with a sort of ocular wit which made words unnecessary.

I turned the page and there was the photograph of Padre Woods, biretta-ed, bespectacled, frail and pensive, gazing down at the model of a ship. It was a terrible contrast. Old age and suffering bring these changes inevitably; but the juxtaposition made me wonder whether the sadness sprang from the change in service, God being a less satisfactory master than His Majesty the King. Was the real story of Alex Woods that of a man who had made a ghastly mistake which he was too loyal to repudiate? From what Stride had said the answer was obviously negative. Woods had found what he wanted in his ministry at the Red Ensign Club. The choice of photograph was Williamson's. He must have a feeling for the dramatic which at times over-ruled the strictly accurate.

I looked across at him and Boston. They were arguing

34

about the releases. "I'll sign any number of releases, chum," Williamson was saying, "but you couldn't expect the Committee—why should *they* give you a blank cheque?" He was using quite a different voice, a conversational tone in which one could detect that he had been born and bred in the East End. I discovered later that he had been trained in elocution, and the voice which he had used when he came in was the one he employed in church. It was of great power and richness and he could throw it to reach every corner of his church. Outside church he alternated between the conversational and the declamatory, choosing the latter unconsciously when he was uncertain of his ground.

When the conversation came back to the revelation at Jutland, Williamson's voice again became declamatory. My suggestion had been working in his imagination and he gave it back to me, enlarged and enriched.

"I can see it in the film, can't you?" he said.

"But is it *true*?" I asked. My eye caught a quotation in the Parish Magazine from the *Church Times* obituary. "Listen to this. 'His call to the priesthood came to him during the Battle of Jutland, about which he rarely spoke, for he hated publicity.'" There were two initials at the end of the obituary. "Who is J.W.?"

"Joseph Williamson," he answered. "And it's true. He loathed publicity."

"And he would have hated a book about himself," I said, "and even more a film." I suspected that for some reason Father Williamson wanted a book—or even more a film—made about his late curate.

His answer was frank. The Padre would have hated to be the subject of a book or film while he was alive. But if a book or film about him could help God, then he would have agreed.

This seemed reasonable. Humility carried beyond that point would have become arrogant.

35

"And yet I'm frightened," said Williamson. "He was so very gentle and undramatic . . . of course, I'll do all I can to help . . . but they mustn't, they really mustn't make him out to be the sort of person that he wasn't."

I looked towards Boston. I knew how embarrassed he was. He could give no guarantee of what the film company would do, because they did not know what they would do, if anything. From what he had said to me, I knew he believed that it would come out all right. I had been a bad person to team with. I could see the canker in the bud, the fortune which he was persuaded might come from this idea and the appalling risks he might run to get it.

He began to talk about what happened with films. An actor X played the part of the person A and everybody who knew A was outraged. But the millions who did not know A were inspired by what X made him out to be.

Boston might be an American blundering in an English set-up. But oddly enough, he was the one man of faith. Hugh and Eucharis Woods, Stride and Williamson believed in the Holy Trinity, but the evangelist was Edward Boston who had gone to Pieter Paulus and sold him with an incredible newspaper story the idea of a film on Padre Woods. I was not sure what Boston believed about God. I had the impression that he wasn't sure himself. But he did believe in this film, not just as a means of making money, but as a power for good.

This impressed me, even though I could adduce his embolism as a reason for the desire to serve God, and the desire to serve God was thus self-interested. The fact remained. Boston had faith.

But I hadn't. "The whole thing seems to me to hinge on what the Padre meant by saying 'it was no earthly command'," I said. "The only person who could tell me that is Lettice Woods."

36

CHAPTER THREE

IT was a couple of days before I could arrange to see Lettice Woods. In the meantime I pondered the absurd film-book proposition. I disapproved on principle of a hard-cover book being commissioned with an eye on the film to be made from it. The revelation at Jutland, without which no film company would be interested, still seemed to me a fake. Unless the testimony of Lettice Woods was strong, I should have to report that there had been no revelation and the film company would withdraw its option-money.

I did not hold high hopes of the fortune which Boston kept expatiating on. For every film that is made, ten or twenty options are taken. But the option-money was essential to the writing of a good and honest book. I should have to get details of his naval career from such of his shipmates as were not dead; and the Royal Navy is not only the Senior, but also the Silent Service. For the later years in the East End I should have to depend on the testimony of people who had neither the words nor the training to express their thoughts. *No Earthly Command* would take a long time and more money than any publisher would be prepared to advance. It was a case of No Film Option, No Book.

I was not sure whether I would mind if there was no book. The detective work of tracking down the revelation would be fun, but not very profitable if it proved to be a fake. I had grown too old to enjoy exposing phony miracles. Even if it were true, the twenty years which

Alex Woods had spent as a Padre in the Sailors' Home interested me more. How could anyone choose such a life, without any of the aesthetic or intellectual escapes which might have made it tolerable? The answer of course was the Love of God. But what was the Love of God?

The Love of God had become a *cliché* to me and it sounded like a *cliché* on the lips of Christians I had met who used it. At one time that would have been sufficient reason for me to dismiss it as nonsense. But I had reached the age when I recognized that phrases become *clichés* because they are true, vivid and accurate; "as quick as lightning", "as cold as ice", "as quiet as the grave". How pleased must have been the men who first coined the small change of description.

The worn phrases of Christianity, valuable though they might have been when they were first minted, seemed to me to have become debased. Those who used them—and there were not many among those I knew—handed them out like wads of grubby notes in an inflation.

Woods attracted me because to him these texts, these prayers and liturgies had their original value. Studying his life would be like going back to the original text instead of reading versions full of corruptions unconsciously introduced by ignorant copyists.

I felt a qualm at undertaking such a work, not being a Christian myself. Theologians would find what I had to write of his religious life as ridiculous as the men of the Royal Navy would find what I wrote of his time in the Senior Service. But there was something to be said for an outside view. Lives of many saints written by the initiated are unreadable, because the authors write in a jargon which is a sort of religious shorthand.

There were many people in the same position as I was. They tried the human recipes for understanding life such as psychoanalysis, Marxism, social-democratic socialism, and found them all inadequate. Experience compelled a belief in a first cause, a law implicit in Nature which could be disobeyed only at one's own cost. But the idea of a personal God, who begot a Son by the Virgin Mary, the belief that Jesus Christ gave His life that we should be saved, the story that He rose from the dead and ascended into heaven, after having performed in His lifetime a staggering number of miracles including walking on the water and raising the dead, were utterly unacceptable. It was as incredible as it would have been to Pontius Pilate that a man could fly through the air faster than the speed of sound.

I had often been told by friends I respected and evangelists I despised that an act of faith was necessary and then all was plain. "That is very nice, if you can make the act of faith," I said, "but I'm afraid that's something I can't do. I have a certain intellectual integrity." When I was younger I had felt a certain pride, not entirely free from smugness, in this answer. Now I was not so sure that I was Master of my Fate, and Captain of my Soul!

If I wrote the life of Alex Woods, I decided, I would write it for the many people in the same position as I was, who had too much intellectual integrity to accept the childish anthropomorphic ideas of Christianity, but who nevertheless were prepared to sympathize and make common cause with good Christians in the defence of civilization against the prevalent barbarisms, despite the intellectual frailty which made them rely on God. "In our present climate there is more need for faith than ever there was," I thought of reporting to the publisher, "and less reason for it. In this life of Alex Woods, I want to express the quandary of the serious agnostic." Then I remembered Alex Woods's mouth, humorously drawn down at the ends and those deep-set eyes twinkling with interior amusement. He might laugh at this proposal, I thought. But if he did, it would be at me, because his

39

life was not concerned with things like this. Or perhaps the eyes would grow hard, the mouth straight and he would be coldly angry.

I was relieved that he was dead. His anger must have been frightening when he disapproved. I was sure that he would have disapproved of me. Yet this would have been an error of narrowness on his part. Honest doubt was more respectable than intellectual dishonesty. If the Padre was as wise as Stride had said, he would certainly have understood that, even if he echoed the words his brother Hugh had put in his mouth, "Why pick on me?"

That was as far as I could go until I had seen Lettice Woods.

My appointment was for tea at the Vicarage in Down Street, Mayfair. I rang the bell and the door was opened by a woman in her early thirties who was obviously Lettice. She had the same features that predominated in Hugh and Alex, the long, thin nose and arching nostrils, the deep-set eyes, the thin, down-curving mouth.

We went into the study and for a time talked around the subject, trying to get each other's measure. I thought she was intelligent—which is of course merely another way of saying that our estimates of people were very similar. This pleased me because I had the impression that it was not possible to discuss people frankly with Christians. So many Christians appeared to invoke charity in order to cover the faults of those of whom they approved and moral judgments to condemn those they could not understand. Lettice Woods could assess people without being censorious.

"The person you must see is Dr Bullitt," she said. "He was Uncle Alex's greatest friend down in the East End. Of course Mr Stride knew more of Uncle—they worked together every day. But Dr Bullitt, the Beloved Physician as Uncle called him, was his friend. He went there every

Sunday to lunch and after lunch they'd sit and talk and perhaps Uncle would fall off to sleep. It was really his home—the only sort of home he had, that is, during all the years he was working in Dock Street."

"And what's the attitude of Dr Bullitt to a life of your uncle?"

"When he heard of the project of a film, he was horrified," she said. "And an American film too. He hasn't met Mr Boston. If he had, I think he would have been surprised to find him so quiet-spoken, and a man of taste."

"He won't surrender the miracle of Jutland without a struggle," I said. "And Father Williamson seems to think you know the truth about it."

"That is going a bit far," she answered. "I saw a copy of that article. Not at the time, of course. I only knew Uncle Alex when I came to London after the War. And most of the time, you must understand, he was just Uncle Alex. It's really only since he died that I realize that he was a saint. To me he was just a dear old gentleman who came to need me. Mr Stride would ring me up to say that my uncle had been asking for me, wondered if I was well. And then I would go down to see him and we'd sit and talk or I'd read him one of his favourite books, *Don Camillo* perhaps, or the William books."

"I can't understand an old gentleman of seventy adoring *Just William*—or, for that matter, reading any works of fiction over and over again."

"He never tired of them. And also *Winnie the Pooh*. You know, in some ways he never grew up. And yet in spirit he was very wise."

It took all sorts to make a world, "Go on," I said, "tell me about Jutland."

"As I say, I showed the article to Uncle Alex and asked him if it was true. He looked at it and handed it back. All he said was, 'Well, it was no earthly command.' What that meant . . . your guess is as good as mine."

"But you have a guess?"

"I think something must have happened at the Battle of Jutland," she said; "otherwise he would just have said that the whole thing was nonsense."

"Surely it can't have been a call to take Holy Orders, or he wouldn't have waited sixteen years before obeying it."

"It must have been connected with the battle."

"But quite definitely he said, 'It was no earthly command'?"

"Quite definitely," she said. "Of course you never knew how serious Uncle Alex was. He loved jokes. He might have meant it in a very different way."

I passed on to the routine questions. Were there any letters, papers, diaries, sermons?

She confirmed what her Uncle Hugh had said. Uncle Alex had never written her anything but the briefest notes, except on one occasion. It was after she had been to see him at the Sailors' Home and they had had an argument about religion, Lettice putting the evangelical position and her uncle the Anglo-Catholic. She showed me the letter and I read it.

My dear Lettice,

I have not written before, as I thought from your letter that you might be coming over—now lest you should think I was "up the pole" *re* your remarks, please don't think that for a moment. I quite agree with what you say. I have every respect for the sincere Low Churchman, only I feel that in the A.C. Way there is more help for ordinary sinners such as myself. I certainly find great help in the Blessed Sacrament Reserved as an aid to devotion. I believe wholeheartedly in Voluntary Confession as a Source of Comfort to the penitent; and also as a means of leading people (the Respectable Pharisees) to realize that respectability is not Christianity—and that many a poor drunkard or prostitute may be nearer to Christ than the unforgiving—unloving—however sober—moral, etc., I am very thankful that you have found Jesus in your way.

"How could he sincerely regard himself as an 'ordinary sinner'?" I asked.

"I suppose that's what made him a saint," his niece said.

"And this is all?" In this short letter there was so much, the tenderness of an uncle for his niece, the fear that through some misunderstanding he might be deprived of her visits, the respect for her own way to God, the vindication of his, the wisdom and tolerance of a mature man and the slang of a schoolboy. "Are you sure there's nothing more?"

"There is something more," she said. "There's an old tuckbox down in Alverstoke, full of Uncle Alex's diaries. I should think the entries were pretty brief, knowing him. But they might help you."

I asked her whereabouts in Alverstoke they were.

"They're in the lumber-room of my father's flat," she said. "And that's another part of Uncle Alex's story. The Chief Petty Officer in charge of wireless on the *Iron Duke* during the First War was a man named G. V. Northcote; and after the War when Uncle Alex was convalescing, Northcote came along and asked for advice. What he should do now the War was over. Uncle told him to set up as a builder in Alverstoke and put it around among the people we knew that he was a good man. Northcote did very well, made quite a lot of money and among other things bought house property in Alverstoke. You know, the sort of houses which my grandfather and his friends lived in, but we can't afford. Northcote turned them into flats and let my father have one at a very reasonable rent, I think all because of Uncle Alex."

"Perhaps he would know about the 'unearthly command'."

"He might. And there are a lot of other things he could tell you about."

Stride had told me that the Padre had been wearing

irons when he first came to the Sailors' Home. I asked Lettice Woods whether she knew when the disease had started.

Her uncle had said that it had come on gradually. He had always been clumsy on his feet, like many of his family. On two occasions he had fallen into the sea when he was a midshipman. And once he fell flat in front of the Commander. But it did not get bad till much later. When he was at the Admiralty, he was so ashamed of his walk that he used to come in by a side entrance to avoid attracting attention. It was a great delight to walk in St. James' Park during the luncheon hour or after work in the evening. But he became self-conscious about doing so and steered a course to avoid the scrutiny of people sitting on the park benches. It wasn't that he was embarrassed by the disability, but he was afraid that people would think that he was drunk and disgracing the King's uniform.

I asked Lettice at what period her uncle had been at the Admiralty. She did not know. Her memory of what he had told her was good, but she was too young to have any sense of comparative history; and why indeed should she want to know what her uncle was doing when she was in rompers?

She said that before the accident in which he broke his femur, her uncle never mentioned his legs. He used them so vigorously that many people did not realize that anything was wrong with them. Those that did not know something was wrong had no idea how exhausted he became by the end of a hard day. "But anyway you can find out about the disease from Dr Hierons of University College Hospital. He made a study of it."

At this point Lettice's boss, the Reverend Howard Marshall, Vicar of Christchurch, Down Street, announced that tea was ready in the next room.

Howard Marshall had himself met with some fearful

accident which had upset the whole balance of his body. He moved in a strange way and I suspected often with great pain. But soon I lost all consciousness of his disabilities, because his personality dominated his body. I asked him what *he* made of Alex Woods.

"He was a saint," said Howard Marshall. "I didn't agree with him of course on matters of ritual—he was too High for me. I'm not sure how successful he was as a priest; or chaplain to the Red Ensign Club. But he was holy. There's not the least doubt he was a very holy man. A good man. Whether he was a great man or a *great* saint . . ."

He proceeded to draw some distinctions, which I did not follow, because I was comparing the mealy-mouthed approach I had made to my namesake, expecting some pietistic platitude, and here he was assessing the Padre's character from half a dozen different angles, comparing his saintliness with that of others, as a connoisseur might for the benefit of a tyro bring out the merits of a painting by comparison with others hanging in the same room. This was all done, not in that hushed voice as if God the Father was having a nap after the Sunday roast beef and Yorkshire, but in a voice trained to cover the wastes of Bisley, Bagshot and Chelsea Barracks without a microphone.

I brought up the question of an unhappy love affair. Eucharis Woods had hinted at it and her husband had certainly not denied it. "Uncle Alex did say something; and so did my father. Yes, my father was very indignant about it all. But why I don't remember."

I said, "It's very difficult to care much about love affairs that were over before one was born."

"It's also very difficult," said the Vicar, "looking back on the pattern of one's life, to remember what it was like looking forward, before the pattern was made."

"I'm not conscious of making a pattern," I said. "Most

45

of us are like Alice, struggling in seas of our own tears. That's what I like about your Uncle Alex. He shed no tears to swim in."

"There were plenty shed by others down at the Club," said Lettice, "when the bar closed and there was nothing to do but think."

I turned to the Vicar. "I've got an idea," I said. "Perhaps this is nonsense. Because all this is in a sphere quite outside my experience. But isn't this rather an interesting sort of test case. Everybody admits that Alex Woods was a saint. In that case shouldn't we be able to see in Alex's life God's purpose sometimes over-ruling Alex's purpose in order to bring him into, shall we say, a more useful sphere of work?"

"That's very possible," said the Vicar. "In my experience it's only at comparatively rare moments that one gets a perception of the Divine Purpose. But it might very well happen; as, after all, you must yourself have experienced—you want something desperately, shall we say. You don't get it, or you get it in a way you don't want it. So you reject it, and find that what has happened instead is far better than what you had planned."

"It's an attractive idea, but of course it's absolute nonsense," I said. "If Alex Woods is really the saint in whose life the purpose of God is to be seen over-riding, why should he be thrown to the wolves as soon as he's dead?"

"What do you mean by 'thrown to the wolves'?"

"Well, there may have been some mystical experience at Jutland, but not the way it said in that obituary notice. Now as soon as Boston reads that lie—and whatever happened, the form it's presented in is a lie—as soon as Boston reads it, he goes to Ultramontane Films Inc. And once again, Ultramontane Films Inc. are interested not in Alex, but in the lie. After all, that seems the only dramatic thing about him. In both these cases the motive is not primarily religious, but money-making. I can't see how anybody could believe that God was behind this."

"Why not?"

"But it's . . . it's inconceivable. To say nothing of being dishonest."

"I didn't mean that God would cause the telling of a lie," said the Vicar. "But he might use a lie once it was told."

"I wasn't thinking of that," I said. "I mean commercially dishonest. The book can't be written without an option having been taken on the film rights. But when the book is written it'll probably be plain that Alex's life was just the opposite of that sensational nonsense they dished up in the obituary. Ultramontane Films Inc. stand to lose five thousand dollars. Just because the Almighty wanted to use that lie."

"In that case," said Howard Marshall, "I'd say it was God mitigating the effects of a lie. A journalist makes up this terrible story. Of course the obituaries copy it. Of course Mr Boston clips it. Of course the film company is interested. That is the impetus of the original lie."

"I'll go further," I said; "the lie and the interest which the lie arouses are not evil; they are just utterly misguided, the sort of nonsense which people will believe who have lost contact with God but want to regain it by a short cut."

"Perhaps," said the Vicar, rather impatient at my breaking in on his train of thought, "when I talk of 'using the lie', it would be truer to say that we don't know what He intends. But things seem to me already fairly well under control. After all, if you turn the book down, Hart-Davis won't do it, and that might mean the whole project is dropped. But if you do decide to write the book it's quite certain that it won't be a sensation-piece."

I did not take the argument further. I was distracted by the idea that it was possible to combine free will with a Divine Purpose. Boston could have ignored the obituary. That would be consistent with God's will, if it was not His intention that something should be written about Alex. Ultramontane Films Inc. could have turned the idea down, as most hard-headed men of business would have done. In saying that he was interested if there was a hard-cover book, Pieter Paulus had made a limited act of faith. He had *chosen* to believe in the possibility of a film.

I had remarked the coincidence that had led Tony Veiller to suggest me as writer and Milton Waldman to nominate me as the investigator. Howard Marshall would say this was not coincidence and if I said that I had the liberty to choose whether or not the book was written, he would agree and point out that the freedom was limited to saying "Yes" or "No". If I said "Yes", I had no choice. The sacred duty of a writer was to discover and tell the truth to the best of his ability. From Howard Marshall's point of view that would be good enough for God.

I looked at Lettice. She was taking seriously what I had intended as a joke, God's participation in this film-book deal. It astonished and pained me. We had talked with such sympathy and mutual understanding that it was sad our ways should part at this point. Yet it was as impossible for me to follow these two through the labyrinths of their credulity as it would be for them to understand my scepticism. It was amazing to think that these two adult people, in other ways so sensible and intelligent, could believe that God should take a hand in promoting a film about a man who had shunned publicity all his life. As if God hadn't enough to worry about that really needed his attention!

I noted the address where I could collect the tuckbox and took my leave as soon as possible. I liked them both very much, but if I stayed any longer I could not trust myself not to show that I considered them only partially sane.

That evening, back in the country, I pondered over their views. If they could believe that God so loved the world that He sent His only begotten Son to die for us, it was not strange that they should believe that God should concern Himself with the reputation of a man who so loved God that he lived for Him. What was extraordinary was that they could believe that the Christian myth was historically true. If it were, everything else followed.

Christianity, I thought, was really the strangest manifestation of the religious spirit, because of all the great religions it was the most implausible. It taxed one's faith far more than primitive animism. Yet millions of people, including men and women of the highest intelligence, not only accepted Christian doctrines but regarded them as the greatest and most satisfying of all truths. Had millions of otherwise sane people been religiously mad during the past nineteen hundred years?

That night I read the Gospel according to St Luke, my favourite among the synoptic gospels. Or rather I tried to read it. I had to give it up. I revolted against the feeding of the five thousand, the procession of miracles, the incomprehensible incident of the Gadarene swine. They were more than reason could tolerate. If they happened, why had not everyone believed? And why if God created natural laws, should *He* suspend them supernaturally? Was not the miracle of life itself enough?

Yet this was what these so different people I had met on my inquiry held in common, the silent Brigadier-General, his ebullient wife, their handsome son, the quietly devious Stride, the dramatic Williamson, the accurate Lettice and her rich-voiced employer. If it was a neurosis, how various were the afflicted; and also how happy in their affliction.

I put the New Testament on one side. Mine was not

EC–D

the company of the believers. Alex Woods might have been a saint, but I wasn't going to commit intellectual suicide for him.

I have never pretended that my actions are governed by pure reason. No novelist would be such an ass. We proceed with the help of all our senses and call in reason as a dictator only when we feel threatened by anarchy.

I had set out to see Lettice Woods, convinced that my day's task was to discover what Alex had meant by "no earthly command". On her answer to that would depend whether I wrote the Padre's life or reported negatively to Milton Waldman.

But during the afternoon a change had come over my attitude. The believers thought that the Divine Will was expressed in the lives of those who loved God. I was certain that it would turn out as the case history of a delusion, but to be convincing I would have to explain why Alex Woods had spent twenty years so happy in his delusion that he forgot about the beauties of life and convinced others of the glory of his delusion.

Was it fair to embark on the life of a holy man with such expectations? I decided that it was, on condition that as an agnostic, claiming the indulgence of honest doubt, I did not reject the claims of honest faith. I should have to argue this story on two levels. I could place my own interpretation as an unbeliever, provided that I had first imagined how things would have appeared to Alex, as a believer.

Next day I wrote to my publisher saying that I thought there was a book and I should like to try to write it, though it did not seem to be the sort of book which might be expected from the obituary notice.

PART TWO

CHAPTER FOUR

HAVING written to my publisher, I sat back and waited. The crowd of obligations appeared impossible to satisfy. Alex's friends, relatives and colleagues expected a life more reverent, Boston and Paulus one more dramatic, than I could give them. The only sincere course was to wait and see if the agents and lawyers and publishers and Ultramontane Films Inc. could reach agreement, to leave it, as Howard Marshall no doubt would have said, to Providence.

The only action I took was to visit Alverstoke, to see the place in which Alex had been born and spent much of his life and to collect the tuckbox containing the diaries.

The diaries had been written not by Alex but by his father. They began in 1881, two months after Alex's birth and continued for the next forty-four years. They were hard to decipher. The handwriting varied wildly according to the diarist's pen and mood but was consistently illegible. Some passages defied elucidation, and those I managed to decipher were only obliquely informative. Dr Woods was concerned with exterior things; who went where when and in what weather. There was no need to say for what purpose, because these were only *aide-mémoire*. This was not the story of his life. Yet it would clearly be invaluable. It gave me a chronology of Alex's career during the forty-four most distant years. I could pinpoint where he was during most of the time. It gave me the basis for being wrong about Alex and his family.

Brigadier-General Woods had the training of a soldier, practical, forthright and disdainful of those details which form so important a part of the biographer's stock in trade. If I asked him for a character sketch of his father, his mother or any other member of his family, he would be as uninformative as a war office communiqué in the darkest hours of a campaign. The diaries would give me a basis for speculation, which could be checked against the Brigadier-General's disagreements. The more impudent my blunderings, the more likely that he would be forced out of his reticence to correct them.

The family background is of the utmost importance to the understanding of anyone, whether the subsequent career is the continuation of a family tradition or a revolt against it.

Alex Woods was a conformist. He accepted what he was taught as a child and held to it steadfastly, unless or until he was forced by conviction to make some modification. For this reason the more I found out about the family, the more I could understand Alex himself.

During the months of negotiation, I occupied myself with reading and annotating the diaries, pestering Hugh with queries based on the information I received, trying out theories so as to have them refuted.

Dr Woods came from an old Surrey family, which had traded and farmed in and near Godalming for centuries. Henry Woods and his brother Percy broke with the family tradition, the former by entering the Navy as a surgeon, the latter by going into the Treasury.

Henry's choice was financially unwise. In those days it was regarded as almost axiomatic that a serving officer should have private means. Service pay was based on that assumption. But however wealthy other members of the Woods family may have been, Dr Woods had nothing except what he received as pay and allowances.

In 1868, when he was stationed in Malta, he married

a young woman named Lilian Kennedy, a shy creature, very handsome, with a long, delicate nose, arched nostrils, hooded eyes. The face argued a distinction of personality which she might have achieved through the exchange of a mother's domination for a husband's loving development. Her greatest accomplishment at the time she married was to play the piano and her husband would accompany her on the flute. She may well have had other talents latent, but in her generation ignorance was regarded as the corollary of innocence.

The week that she married, her father Colonel Kennedy died, and her mother decided that she would make her home with Lilian and Henry Woods. Marriage did not liberate the young Lilian. It merely added to a rich and demanding mother a husband, forceful, energetic and intellectually superior to herself. She became too occupied with being a daughter, a wife and a mother ever to have time to become herself.

During the first twelve years of Henry's married life, the Admiralty rolled him round like a stone. The first child, a daughter, was born in Malta. She was christened Lilian after her Mother, Edyth, after a beloved aunt and Tonbella after a revered ancestor. To call her by either of the first two would have caused confusion in the family, to call her by the last would have caused confusion or worse in the child. So she was known, at least to her father, as Bee, until with the death of his sister Edyth that name fell vacant.

By the time the next child was born, a boy called Charles Robert Sandford, the family had moved to Chatham. That was January 1871. In less than fourteen months a second daughter arrived, Kathleen Felicia Devereux. She was born in Royal Buildings, Deal. In Royal Buildings, Walmer, two more sons were born, Arthur Llewellyn and Hugh Kennedy.

Alex, or to give him his full title Alexander Riall

Wadham, was the first and only child to be born in Alverstoke, the place which all the family was to come to regard as home.

At the time that Alex was born, Dr Woods had no idea that it would become a permanent place of residence. The prospect that in the future he would be moved round as frequently as he had been in the past appeared an alarming certainty. The move to Alverstoke had been occasioned by the posting of Staff Surgeon Henry Woods to the Royal Yacht *Osborne*, which was based on Portsmouth. R.Y. *Osborne* was the yacht used by the Prince and Princess of Wales and was employed in the ferrying of distinguished passengers between Portsmouth and Osborne, when Queen Victoria was in residence in the Isle of Wight, and at other times on cruises which combined the royal pleasure with the imperial business.

Dr Woods viewed the prospect of being posted away from the Royal Yacht with alarm, because his sons were reaching the age when their schooling had to be taken seriously. If he had had enough money to send them to a good boarding school, he would not have worried. But even with the contributions which Mrs Kennedy made to the family exchequer, he could afford only a day school, and if they were switched from one day school to another the boys' education would be bound to suffer. (The girls did not matter, because it was not important for a girl to be stuffed full of learning. Their concern was not books but babies.)

He had good reason for alarm. A tour of duty on the royal yachts was regarded by the Admiralty as a pleasant interlude in service life. There was something to be said for personnel having the opportunity to serve their Majesties personally, and for their Majesties to meet as large a number of their naval subjects as possible. It promoted personal loyalty on one side and, it was hoped, royal sympathy for the Senior Service on the other.

There were many reasons against permanent appointments to the royal yachts. After too long in the royal backwaters officers and men would grow soft and unfitted for active service. They would rise by the automatic process of promotion through seniority, so that the cost of the royal yachts would increase every year. Through too long familiarity the officers and crews would come to regard themselves as personal servants of the Royal Family instead of serving men and officers.

Lord Charles Beresford, Captain of the R.Y. *Osborne* when Staff Surgeon Woods joined her, was aware of all these arguments and appealed to the Prince of Wales. The Prince needed little persuasion. In the royal household there were so many old familiar faces, and among his relatives who sat on, or crowded round, the thrones of Europe, so many homely ones, that he welcomed any chance of change. A fresh face and unknown personality promised if not an alleviation of the boredom of being just Bertie to the Queen of England and the Empress of India, at least an alteration of the agony—as when one has stood so long on one foot that one has pins and needles in it, a shift of weight on to the other foot gives relief.

But, luckily for the Woods family, Queen Victoria had reached an age when novelty palled. "I am an old woman now," she told Lord Charles Beresford. "I like to see faces I know about me and not to have to begin again with new faces."

The Queen had grown used to the handsome, honest, bearded face of Staff Surgeon Woods. When he left the R.Y. *Osborne*, it was only to transfer to the Queen's own yacht, the *Victoria and Albert*. There he remained until the end of her days, and if he had had his will he would have remained there until the time of his retirement, with the rank of Inspector-General of Hospitals and Fleets, burdening the overheads of the yacht by occupying a position normally held by a Staff Surgeon, if the Lords

Commissioners of the Admiralty had not insisted on his supercession.

This was all in the future. At the time of Alex's birth, it looked as if the term of appointment would not be more than three years, after which the dreary trek round naval stations would begin again.

Though the Doctor had been married for twelve years, he had acquired practically no family possessions. The cost of moving chattels was too high to make it worth his while. It was better to rent furnished houses, and if extra furniture was needed, to make it himself. When Hugh grew too big for his cot, it was passed over to Alex and the Doctor made a new bed for Hugh. In the enforced idleness of retirement, he compiled a list of articles of furniture which he had made and it filled half a dozen pages.

I imagined that the Doctor had combined the pleasure of a hobby with the needs of economy. I detected a certain pride in an entry for Christmas twenty-six years after his marriage that for the first time the family had sat down to Christmas dinner at their own dining table—one which the Doctor had picked up cheaply secondhand. But according to Hugh Woods, I was wrong. Dr Woods refused to inherit any of his parents' furniture, some of which was so fine that his brother Percy presented it to the Victoria and Albert Museum. Dr Woods seems, therefore, to have been indifferent to the beauty or value of furniture. This makes more understandable the bare utility of Alex's two little rooms in the Sailors' Home. If there had been a tradition in his father's home of objects of beauty, one might have found a trace of it surviving Alex's dedication to God. As it was, Alex did not have to disencumber himself of a love for material things, because he had never possesed it. This was a negative characteristic which he inherited from his father.

Far more important were the positive characteristics

emerging from a comparison of Alex as revealed by his rooms in the Sailors' Home and his father revealed in the pages of his diaries.

There was that picture of Queen Elizabeth II which hung on a wall of his study, "my Queen" as he called her, the devotion to the Royal Family which was more akin to a reverent love than a workaday loyalty. The foundation for that love was laid in infancy. Queen Victoria, her children and grandchildren were not the distant figures to Alex and his brothers and sisters that they were to most English children of their age. They were people whose every movement was followed by their father and whom he felt deeply honoured to serve. The glamour of royalty was enhanced by the fact that the Doctor owed his intimacy with members of the royal household not to birth but to his position on the Royal Yacht. This kept his sense of privilege bright; an utter devotion to his Queen was small recompense for the gracious confidence, the glittering levées at Clarence House, the glimpses into state affairs, the receptions in St Petersburg, Berlin and Brussels, the gaiety of Cowes and those annual fortnights at Balmoral when Dr Woods relieved Dr James Reid as his *locum tenens*.

Dr Woods had an integrated personality. He was intelligent without being an intellectual. He had a varied curiosity, untinged by scepticism. He was conscious of ignorance but unassailed by doubt. To say that he was a simple and unsophisticated man is not to imply that his judgment was not shrewd or his thought sustained. It was rather that in mind and temperament he belonged to the nineteenth century. His faith in the Evangelical Church of England, the House of Hanover and the civilizing mission of the British Empire was unshakeable. He distrusted the Papacy and the Oxford Movement, considered that democracy would inevitably degenerate into socialism, and foresaw the outbreak of the First

59

World War twenty years before it came. He was a monarchist who was almost as critical of the Tory Party as he was of the Liberals. Parliament was rather a mistake. Yet with all his devotion to Christ the King and Victoria the Queen and Empress, he was less class-conscious than most democrats. He believed in a spiritual democracy. Every human creature was possessed of a soul, capable of salvation and equal before God. Every human creature was possessed of a body, the ills of which he would do all in his power as a doctor to cure. In his practice he made no distinction between his Queen and the least of her subjects. Sensible though he was of the gradations of rank in the Service and society, he was equalitarian in church and the sickroom. He was an excellent mixer. To meet kings and emperors was exciting (as it would be to most of us), but that did not make him any less able to get on with the men and women from all walks of life to whom he lectured on First Aid. His audience at Balmoral, where immediately on his first arrival he conducted first aid lectures for men and women, included the future King of England and the coachmen, two princesses, ladies-in-waiting and the domestic staff.

Alex inherited the same qualities from his father. He loved royalty. Queen Elizabeth II was not merely *his* Queen. She was also the great-grand-daughter of the Queen for whom he had been named and who in his childhood had been a sort of radiant super-aunty. Yet at the same time he could joke with old reprobates like the red-biddy-drinker who lounged at the corner of Dock Street and Cable Street. He was at ease with all sorts and conditions of people, happier in many ways with men of the lower deck than with their officers, yet worshipping Admiral Jellicoe as a hero. In politics he was a High Tory, yet he voted Labour in 1945; only to find that the Welfare State was a poor substitute for brotherly love.

His patriotism would lead him into instinctive bigotries ("the only good German is a dead German") from which, after a moment's reflection, his religion would cause him to retract with a grin.

He was as much a nineteenth-century man as his father; just as Soren Kierkegaard was a twentieth-century man, though he was born in 1813 and died twenty-five years before Alex's birth. Paradoxically Alex Woods was even more like his father than his father was. The characteristics apparent in Dr Woods were passed on to Alex and refined in the process.

Much of the credit for this obviously lay with Dr Woods. He was a man of remarkable equanimity. The presence of his mother-in-law imposed a burden which to many men would have been insupportable. The only indication of the strain in his diaries was that she was listed at the end of each as being in the house, not among the family but as a supernumerary like the servants, the inevitable "Mrs K.", each year a little deafer, a little blinder, a little more forgetful and, I suspect, a little more tiresome.

Yet even Mrs K. had her characteristic legacy for Alex. Deaf as she grew, she could still be read to. Each day someone or other was deputed to bawl out a book close to her ear. Alex had all the "William" books, the works of George A. Birmingham, the Don Camillo books and *Winnie the Pooh* to choose from. He never tired of these favourites. His grandmother was more limited. She had two light Victorian novels, which were read to her alternately, week after week, month after month, year after year. As her hearing failed, the familiarity grew. All she needed was a word here or there in order to retrace the well-worn paths of earlier amusement.

Mrs K. probably felt that she was a minority in the Woods household. To give her support, she brought in her son Llewellyn, who was even more dependent on her than Lilian. Llewellyn was not married, nor was he any more qualified to maintain himself than his sister. An allowance from his mother kept him in attractive idleness. He belonged to the militia, a voluntary organization with a smart uniform, in which he attained the rank of lieutenant-colonel. The militia gave him the maximum of uniform with the minimum of parades. He enjoyed shooting and fishing. He owned good guns and rods and kept a couple of sailing boats in Stokes Bay. He could afford to drink as much as was good for him and sometimes more; and he possessed a largeness of vision of the sort that is found far more frequently among those with unearned incomes than among those who work for their livings.

Like Mrs K., Uncle Llewellyn received only supernumerary mention in the Doctor's New Year's Eve lists. He was more than anyone in the house the outsider. His lilies-of-the-field existence, however unobtrusively he passed it, was a continuous contrast to the Doctor's steady application.

The Doctor and the Lieutenant-Colonel in the militia felt a mutual antipathy, one for the other. It says much for them both that in this small and overcrowded house they never came into open conflict. To have done so would have been destructive and indecorous. The cook, the parlourmaid or the nurse would have overheard them and the scandal would have been whispered through the village.

Their situation was one which existed in nearly every middle-class Victorian household. Their domestic conflict would have been settled easily enough if it had been brought periodically into the open. The presence of servants made it necessary to hush things up, or choose oblique ways for expressing anger. Dr Woods and Lieutenant-Colonel Kennedy never exchanged a cross word, except when Llewellyn ate onions or Henry varnished wood. The Staff Surgeon on the Royal Yacht abominated the smells of onions, fresh, fried, pickled or braised, in all of which forms the Lieutenant-Colonel in the militia adored them. Dr Woods said nothing about Uncle Lewellyn, but from the way that he expressed himself on the subject of onions and onion-lovers there was no need to particularize.

Uncle Llewellyn, I fancy, was more urbane in his counter-attack. With a generalization about how distastes vary, he would carry the discourse into the heart of the varnish country. He might mention the strange visceral insensibility to the odour of varnish which the lac-farmers of Bhutan were reputed to develop. Perhaps the Doctor had some medical explanation for it. Anyway whatever harm was caused by contact with varnish, there must have been something wrong with the Bhutanese farmers to start with for them to choose to cultivate the stuff instead of something useful—like onions.

Shrewd blows were exchanged behind the cover of onions and varnish. But it was all very harmless on the surface, a family joke in appearance and partly in reality.

In their choice of small bones for contention, Henry Woods and Llewellyn Kennedy were no different from thousands of their middle-class contemporaries. When I was a young man, I thought it a hypocritical evasion of real conflict. Now I am less sure. A symbolic squabble can provide the safety-valve for emotions which could cause permanent damage if openly expressed. Even psychologists who believe that aggression should have free play agree that it is expressed less dangerously on fields of sport than of battle. Considering how boxed up they were at No 3 The Holt, the Woods and Kennedys did well to confine their dislikes to varnish and onions.

There were thirteen people living at No. 3, a tall, narrow, semi-detached house with ten rooms. On the top floor were two large bedrooms and one dressing-room. Charles, Arthur and Hugh slept in the large front bedroom, the two maids in the back, and the nurse and Alex in the little room. On the floor beneath were Dr and Mrs Woods below the boys, Mrs Kennedy and the two girls below the maids, and Uncle Llewellyn below the nurse and Alex. There was no bathroom. Hot water was carried up to the bedrooms for washing and for the rare bath in a painted tin tub in front of the bedroom fire.

On the ground floor there were two large rooms. The front one served as a sitting-room, the back one as a dining-room and study in which the Doctor could make up his accounts, write his reports, letters and diaries and perhaps do his serious reading.

Below in the semi-basement were the kitchen offices and the cellar where were kept Uncle Llewellyn's barrel of ale and Mrs K.'s barrel of porter, which she drank in winter mulled with a sizzling poker taken red hot from the fire at her back.

As the family grew up, the Doctor took the two houses next door, Nos. 1 and 2 The Holt. He knocked them into one and renamed the house West Holt. This gave him eleven bedrooms, a bathroom and four reception rooms, as well as a room to use as a workshop. The congestion was ended. A greater degree of privacy was possible for them all.

One of the first things which had struck me when I went to the Sailors' Home was how Alex had managed to preserve his privacy. Stride had emphasized how available the Padre was. Men had knocked at his door at all hours of the day and night and had never been turned away, unless they had been too drunk to be capable of any coherence (and then the Padre had frequently put them to bed). He had clearly mastered the technique of achieving privacy, while living in a community. His years in the Royal Navy would have taught him that, of course: but I suspect that he had learnt it earlier as the youngest member of a large and crowded household.

But this was in the future. When Alex first arrived at No. 3 The Holt, the overcrowding and the occasional stresses of the family meant nothing to him. He was the centre of his universe, to which came numbers of people of various shapes, scents and sizes, all prepared to make a fuss of the baby. That was the first view.

The second was from the window of the top-floor room where he slept with his nurse, a vision of land and sea and sky which was never the same for two moments, a vision of glory on which the ever-changing light and weather played variations.

These were his first two loves; the family which surrounded him with warmth, and the sea whose mystery lay just beyond his window.

CHAPTER FIVE

When I asked Hugh how he got on with Alex and his other brothers, he said, "I can't remember ever having had a quarrel with Alex when we were boys; and at the same time I can't remember a day when Arthur and I didn't fight."

"Of course you and Alex were next to one another in age," I said; "I suppose it was natural that you should be closer to one another than the rest."

"At that age," Hugh agreed; "but later on, when we were all grown up and differences in years didn't mean so much, Charles and Alex were very close. When Alex was at the Red Ensign Club, he always spent his holidays with Charles and his wife Dorothy—except right at the end, when Charles grew infirm. Then he came to stay with Eucharis and me."

In this account Hugh and Charles divided Alex's sympathies between them—as far as the brothers were concerned—and there was no great bond between Alex and Arthur. But when I visited Arthur, who was in a nursing home struggling to sort out the threads that had got tangled in his brain as a result of a stroke, he was emphatic that Alex and he were the greatest friends as boys. "We were both Navy," he said, "just as Charles and Hugh were both Army."

As a boy Arthur Llewellyn Woods loved messing about with his uncle's and any other boats he could get hold of. He loved fishing and he told me a long story about Alex and himself getting caught by a storm on Southampton

Water and having to sail back to Alverstoke against all advice, because Alex had to return to his training ship and Arthur's creed was to bring his craft to home port at all costs.

As a boy Arthur never contemplated going to sea. Uncle Llewellyn had said, "Of course every penny of mine will be yours one day, my dear boy. But meanwhile you've got your fortune to make." Like so many people living on unearned income, Uncle Llewellyn considered himself an authority on making a fortune. "Food!" he said. "People must eat. That's where the money lies."

When Arthur pointed out that a good farm cost a lot of money, his uncle laughed. "Go west, young man. In Canada they're just giving land away. The first year you cover your cost, your farming equipment, your bare living expenses. The next year you show a profit. And by the time you're my age, you've retired with your pile, a man of leisure able to devote himself . . . well, you won't have to carve inkstands as a pastime and fill the place with the stench of varnish."

I strongly suspect that the uncle, Lieutenant-Colonel Llewellyn Kennedy of the Militia, if he had been driven to make a fortune for himself, would have got no further than selling gold bricks in Piccadilly. But for his nephew he suggested a slice of the Canadian cornbelt, to be acquired for a song.

Arthur took up the idea with enthusiasm. He was intrigued by his uncle's decorative idleness. His father's preoccupation with making a small salary go a long way appeared dull and unimaginative. Uncle Llewellyn had vision.

Dr Woods loved all his children. He hated being thrust into an ungenerous role. If Arthur was resolved to become a Canadian farmer, he would do his best to help him. But he was hard pressed for money and there were five other children to consider. With the aid of his brother Percy, he raised a small grubstake for his son and saw him off on the boat to Canada, his heart heavy with misgivings. He had done his best.

But his best was totally inadequate. Arthur lacked experience and maturity. If he had been older and wiser, he would have admitted the certainty of defeat even before he started. As it was, he was back within a year, having lost the few pounds he took with him but even more convinced of the possibilities of Canada, if he was adequately financed.

Dr Woods listened and asked him how much he wanted. Young Arthur cut his requirements to the minimum. His father advanced his grubstake to the maximum, which was far below what Arthur knew he required. But Arthur recognized that he was being offered more than all the rest and he must make do with what his father could afford. He was an optimist and perhaps something would turn up.

He had no reserve against misfortune and very soon he was begging for more money and cashing cheques sent by his father ahead of their time for presentation. Dr Woods saw only that Arthur was asking for more than he could afford and more than the rest of his children combined were getting. Arthur saw only how pitiably inadequate were the remittances which his father seemed to consider munificent. Far from being grateful, young Arthur wrote his father a recriminating letter.

It arrived at Alverstoke and gave the Doctor an appalling shock. He had been used to living in a temperate climate of love, and this was like a blast off the ice-cap. He hovered for several days before replying and then wrote sadly back that he had never imagined that Arthur should think such things of him.

It is the only record of disharmony which I discovered in the forty-four years of diaries. But from then on, the father's entries about Arthur changed. What had been anxiety became tinged with disappointment, even at times a shade of bitterness. He still lent his aid to schemes of farming and fishing; but it was not until Arthur joined the Royal Canadian Navy that he was restored to favour.

The rest of the family sided with Dr Woods, with the exception of Alex. He, though the most devoted and exemplary of sons, refused to condemn his brother. He could imagine the sort of stresses under which Arthur had laboured, making his lonely losses on the far side of the Atlantic. Arthur had failed, but he had shown an independence and initiative greater than any of the other children; and Alex was always hesitant about passing judgment on another. He probably saw that his brother was the victim of Uncle Llewellyn's dreams of independence.

Uncle Llewellyn himself was beyond the range of the Doctor's displeasure. Though considered by everyone a confirmed bachelor, he suddenly announced his engagement to a farmer's daughter, on marrying whom he removed to Lowestoft in East Anglia. Thenceforth he severed contact with the Woods family, until he was on his deathbed. As he lay dying, he was asked if there was anyone he wished to see; and the person he requested was not his sister nor his favourite nephew Arthur but the old Doctor, with whom he had battled over onions and varnish.

Most of us learn tolerance and understanding through our own commission of errors. We have to make the mistakes ourselves, because we are convinced that we are somehow different from other people. It seems to me that Alex was different from other people in being convinced he was like them. This conviction enabled him to learn from the experiences of others and to give those in trouble a greater sympathy than they received from the average self-engrossed man. Arthur's statement that he and Alex had an especially close bond, because they were both in the Navy, was, I suspect, inaccurate. I believe that the close bond was established during the troublous years of Canadian farming and fishing, before Arthur joined the Royal Canadian Navy, and that in truth Arthur felt closer to Alex than to any other member of his family. The converse was not true. Alex had the genius to establish a closer bond with every member of his family than the others had.

On whatever else they may be unclear, his father's diaries reveal how this youngest of his children came to occupy a special place of love and trust in his father's heart. Dr Woods loved all his children deeply, treating them from the beginning with the respect due to human personalities, even if young and immature. He was also a just man, free from favouritism. The extra love which Alex evoked was something beyond his father's control, springing from a depth of parental passion which can be tapped only by the child itself.

Having said that, one must admit that Alex's choice of a naval career materially strengthened this special love. At his departure for the *Britannia* as a cadet, he became for the first time "dear old Alex", and remained so, only dropping the affectionate "old" as he ceased to be young. The other children were called simply by their Christian names, except on rare occasions.

It surprises me less that Alex chose the Navy than that the other brothers failed to do so. Alverstoke was a dull and unattractive village in itself. Its excitement lay in its views of the sea, its closeness to the busiest waterway in the world. From the window of his second-floor bedroom Alex could look out across Stokes Bay to the Isle of Wight and Spithead and see the continuous traffic of ships, small craft such as his Uncle Llewellyn's sailing boats, fishing smacks, tubs and dinghies. There were the great yachts of kings and millionaires which came each year to Cowes; and all the year round there was the coming and going of the ships of the Channel Fleet based on Portsmouth, men-of-war which were obsolescent as fighting vessels and were being slowly replaced. And there were the great, ocean-going Atlantic liners steaming to and from Southampton.

Even the everyday routine of the Royal Navy at work in the harbour was calculated to fire a boy's heart with love of a life more colourful and adventurous than a landsman's, yet in some ways more secure, demanding less lonely enterprise. Sights and sounds which did not pall with familiarity were the plying of small boats, voices carrying over water commands as strange as magic and more effective, sailors ashore advertising their ships with their hatbands and the Royal Navy with their smartness, the annual wonder of Portsmouth Navy Week and the introduction of the people to the fleet which protected them. There were the annual manœuvres, the mock battles of the Blue Fleet and the Red. There were the special occasions, goodwill visits of foreign squadrons, royal inspections by potentates who had to be impressed without their gaining secret information. Finally and most exciting of all was the Golden Jubilee review at Spithead, mile upon mile of ships as far as the eye could see, the assembly of emperors, kings and princes, magnificent from a distance, yet humanized by the Doctor's accounts of intimate little conversations.

Apart from these Royal Naval occasions, there was the regular business plied daily by the white paddle-steamers ferrying backwards and forward between the mainland and the Isle of Wight, and the less frequent passage of the great passenger steamers, taking the eastern passage to Southampton to avoid the dangerous Needles, floating cities that seemed the unsinkable triumph of modern engineering until the *Titanic* made her maiden voyage.

Dr Woods had a magnificent telescope with which he

71

scanned the sea by day and the heavens by night. All the boys learnt to use it, and long before he went to the *Britannia* Alex was expert in the recognition not only of every class of ship, but of each individual ship in her class.

Being in the upper front rooms of the houses in the Holt was like standing on the bridge of a ship placed temporarily in dry-dock. No one could look out without feeling the urge to leave the dull land and sail those exciting waters on a craft that answered to wind and sail and helm. Born and bred in those high houses, Alex came to have the sea in his blood. It was never to be ignored. In springtime there was the sunlight chasing the shadows of clouds across the broken water, in breathless August the great yachts angling for a puff of wind to catch the canvas, and in winter, with the blinds drawn and the heavy curtains pulled, there were the great winds off the Channel roaring down the chimneys.

Even to someone unconnected with the Royal Navy, the veriest landlubber, a prey to sickness immediately he steps aboard, the sea around Alverstoke calls up the Francis Drake fantasies. He is tempted to bark like a sea-dog.

To Alex the nautical confraternity was like a club. His father was a respected member and he himself could join as soon as he reached a suitable age. He had begun his training long before he sat for the *Britannia* examination. The Royal Navy was part of the fabric of his infancy and childhood.

I suspect that in so far as he made a conscious choice of a career, he opted for the Navy because he admired his father and loved the non-aggressive aspects of the naval life, the smartness, the reassuring routines, the open air, the sea and the friendliness of the naval men he met. His father had gloomy forebodings about the imminence of Britain's hour of danger and Alex had no hesitation about fighting for his king and country when the time came. But its attraction in peacetime was its leisure, sport, healthiness and variety.

Dr Woods was at Balmoral when Alex sat for the *Britannia* examination. Alex reported each day how he thought he had done. There was no false modesty. In the first day's papers he considered he did well, in the remainder well enough.

He was quite right. There were a hundred and thirty entrants for the sixty vacancies and Alex came out seventeenth. He had got his foot on the first rung of the ladder.

His father was filled with pride, which soon gave way to anxiety. He knew that it was a very slippery ladder. The casualties can be seen from a paper which I discovered in one of Alex's scrapbooks. H.M.S. *Britannia* issued periodic bulletins reporting on the progress made by each "term" of cadets; and this paper was a bulletin issued in 1919 giving the history of Alex and the fifty-nine other cadets of his term.

Of the sixty cadets, one died on the *Britannia* and one was invalided out. One was dismissed and joined the Merchant Navy. Two failed to pass out.

Of the fifty-five who survived their cadetship, one resigned in 1901 to avoid trial, the services of a second were dispensed with, a third was dismissed the service by court martial and a fourth deserted for ten months, returned to the service and then retired and took Holy Orders.

Of the fifty-one left, four were killed or drowned before August 1914 and eight retired, one of whom was found drowned a few months later.

Of the thirty-nine who were still in the Service at the outbreak of the First World War, only two were killed on active service. Tragically, one of these was the most brilliant cadet of the term, J. B. Waterlow, who entered the *Britannia* fifth and passed out first with 2,138 marks out of a possible 2,500. Seven officers of the term gained D.S.O.'s and one a C.M.G.

Dr Woods was not averse to pulling strings. When Hugh had sat for a cadetship at Sandhurst, he was informed that he had just failed. Dr Woods immediately paid a hasty visit to his old friend Miss Knollys, who as an intimate of the Queen knew many people who wished to please her. He discussed the possibility of Hugh having one of the Queen's special cadetships. As luck would have it, the journey was not necessary. Entrants for Sandhurst were not medically examined until after the written examination, and enough entrants were failed on their medical to give Hugh his place on his own merits.

For Alex Dr Woods could and did pull many more strings. He was worried about the *Britannia*. It was the only training establishment for naval officer cadets. But there had been a scandal about the way the older cadets bullied the younger. The *Britannia* consisted of two old sailing ships joined by a gangway and achored in the lovely shelter of Dartmouth Harbour.

The teaching was reputed to be poor. But since that would be the same for all, it did not worry the Doctor. What filled him with misgiving was the overcrowding. Two hundred and forty cadets were crowded into the living space originally designed for a hundred and fifty. It would scarcely have been planned differently if its purpose had been the spread of infectious disease.

Sure enough, though Alex was supposed to join on 4 September 1894, the term had to be postponed because of a whooping cough scare. When Alex finally went, his father accompanied him. What was the point of being an Inspector-General of Hospitals and Fleets, if he could not meet the Medical Officer, see over the sick bay and make certain that if Alex fell ill he would get the best attention?

While he was there, he called on the Captain and the Commander for a chat. If there had been any doubt about the identity of Cadet Woods, it had been dispelled by the time Inspector-General Woods returned to Portsmouth to attend his Queen and her royal guests aboard the *Victoria and Albert*.

This practice of string-pulling was another thing which Alex took over from his father in later life. At the Sailors' Home he worked wherever possible through personal contacts. His circle of acquaintance was extensive. When someone came to him in distress, he would pick up the telephone and get help as a personal favour. It was the most effective way of making the old charity system work. But after the Second World War it drove the Padre into opposition to the Social Services. He tried to bypass them instead of working through them and humanizing them.

Some of the shipmates who sailed with Alex at a later stage in his career criticized Dr Woods for having tried to smooth his son's path in the Royal Navy. They thought Alex would have done better if he had had to fight his way. It is not for me to judge. It was the form which the Doctor's love took. The parting filled him with sadness and he noted in his diary, "Very down myself, but Alex quite cheery."

Alex was probably just as "down", but he was determined to reassure his father by putting on a good face. He had a story of one of his later departures to the *Britannia*, when his parents saw him off to Dartmouth at Stokes Bay station. Alex felt close to tears, but he brought a copy of the sporting periodical the *Pink 'Un* to demonstrate his carefree mood. No reader of the *Pink 'Un* could possibly burst into tears when saying good-bye.

Alex stayed at the compartment window, sustaining the trivialities of a railway farewell, clutching this talisman. Suddenly the railway engine belched forth smoke and a small coal landed in Alex's eye. The eye began to water, using in order to get rid of this foreign body tears which he had been keeping back.

At that moment the train began to draw out. As it did so, Alex waved the *Pink 'Un* frantically and found himself actually laughing with relief at being able to discharge his grief.

I had reached about this stage in my investigation, when the business negotiations were completed and the releases signed by the family. The news filled me with panic. The Doctor's diaries told me a great deal about Alex's father and the forms his love for Alex had taken. They revealed a simple, religious, loving, emotional and intelligent naval surgeon with characteristics which his son had taken over and raised to the power of sainthood. But how could one make a book about this? Where was the conflict which as a novelist I looked for in any character I depicted, and as a person I couldn't avoid finding in almost every man or woman I met? Where was the drama? Where were the spiritual crises?

There was a chance that I could learn something from the people with whom he had sailed. The Admiralty Library provided me with a list of those who survived and the ships on which he had served. Including the *Britannia*, Alex had eighteen postings in the course of his thirty-three years in the Navy (1895-1928). He passed out from the *Britannia* sixteenth and was among those given the rank of midshipman while still there. He seems to have been one of the comparatively few of his term who kept a consistent position. Some—presumably those who had been over-crammed to reach the right standard—fell off during their year in the *Britannia*; others spurted ahead. Alex maintained a consistent but not outstanding level.

After a year in the *Britannia*, he spent three years and three months as a midshipman on first-class battleships of the Channel Squadron (H.M.S. *Royal Sovereign*, 15 September 1896–30 June; H.M.S. *Repulse* 1 July–31 December 1899). The Channel Squadron was based on Portsmouth and Alex was able to spend his time ashore at home.

On 1 January 1900 he was promoted to Sub-Lieutenant, sent for courses to the Royal Naval College, Greenwich, and then to a further course on H.M.S. *Excellent*. This gave him his general grounding as an officer. On 14 March 1901 he was posted for ten weeks to the torpedo boat destroyer H.M.S. *Cynthia*, based on Chatham. On 1 June of that year he went to the Mediterranean, where he spent the first eighteen months on the first-class cruiser H.M.S. *Andromeda* and the remainder of his time on H.M.S. *Bacchante*, the flagship of Rear-Admiral Sir Baldwin W. Walker, Bt., C.M.E., of the Cruiser Division of the Mediterranean Fleet.

It is possible that Alex with his great charm, his discretion, thoughtfulness and unobtrusive competence would have secured for himself a rapid advancement. (He was one of the first of his term to be promoted to lieutenant, 1 April 1902.) But it is certain that his father was continually pressing his son's claims on those who might be of assistance.

When Alex returned to England at the end of 1905, it was to take one of the specialist courses, signals, navigation or gunnery, compulsory for all lieutenants after their period of general service. Alex chose signals and was posted as a supernumerary to H.M.S. *Victory*, Portsmouth, for the duration of his course.

He passed out brilliantly and was chosen as Flag Lieutenant by Rear-Admiral Francis Bridgeman. He was in the Mediterranean with Bridgeman for a year and when the Rear-Admiral was promoted to the command of the Home Fleet, Alex went with him to H.M.S. *Dreadnought*.

From then on, until August 1916, Alex was concerned exclusively with signals. Apart from a year which he spent in charge of the Signal School, H.M.S. *Pembroke* at Chatham, the whole of that time was spent in flagships, mostly with the Home and Grand Fleets.

He was made a commander in December 1912. He could rise no higher as a signals officer, and in 1916 he was given command of the light cruiser H.M.S. *Topaze*. He remained in command of the *Topaze* until he was invalided home in April 1919. In June of that year, he was promoted to the rank of Captain. No job was found for him until 26 April 1920, when he went to the Admiralty as Secretary to the President of the Naval Inter-Allied Commission of control of Germany.

He went back to sea in August 1922, in command of the destroyer repair ship, H.M.S. *Greenwich*. Two years later he was appointed to the command of his last ship, H.M.S. *Concord*, a cruiser which he took on an exchange visit to Australia. From there they were ordered to the China station, where he handed over his command and transferred to H.M.S. *Diomed*, the vessel which the *Concord* had come to relieve.

When Alex had brought the *Diomed* home to port, his sea days were over. On 19 October 1925 he was appointed for a Senior Officers' Technical Course at Portsmouth, and in December of the next year he became Captain of Portsmouth Dockyard, Deputy Superintendent and King's Harbourmaster. He held that post until November 1928. He must then have been unemployed, on half pay. The remaining details given by the Admiralty merely record that in 1931 he was promoted to Rear-Admiral on 3 April and placed on the retired list next day, that he was appointed Honorary Chaplain, R.N.V.R. (London Division) on 27 December 1934, promoted to Vice-Admiral on 1 January 1936 and died on 1 November 1954.

Those were the bare bones of his naval career. It remained to be seen whether the admirals, captains, commanders and lieutenants who survived him could give them flesh and blood.

CHAPTER SIX

IT was hard to frame a letter which could be used for all the shipmates on the Admiralty list. In his old age Alex had come to recognize that the first signs of his muscular atrophy had shown themselves when he was still a midshipman. But did he recognize this at the time? When did he recognize it himself? When did his fellow-officers recognize it? Did he manage to keep it secret from the Admiralty?

That was a question which I had to ask everyone. The "interposed message" from Almighty God could only be known, if at all, to those who were with him on the *Iron Duke* during the Battle of Jutland or those who had sailed with him after that.

But these two questions, important though they were, dealt with only minute fractions of the thirty-three years of his active service. Far more important were the details of his everyday life—the biographer's *minutiae*. Few people have any talent for this sort of observation; and even when they have, they exercise it on the famous, the infamous or the eccentric. From what his friends and relatives had told me, Alex would have done or said little that remained in anybody's memory.

The answers to my enquiry began to come in by return of post. The mention of Alex's name evoked an immediate response.

Sammy Woods, as he was known in the Navy from the cricketer who was famous when Alex was in the *Britannia*, had left a very positive impression on everybody who knew him. With three exceptions everybody replied in almost identical terms.

Dear Mr Calder-Marshall,

Yes, I did sail with Sammy Woods on the . . . and of course I met him subsequently on numbers of different occasions which I cannot precisely recall. He was as you know a very religious man. I was not surprised to hear that he had taken Orders. I always thought he was better fitted for the Church than the rough and tumble of the Navy.

He was a brilliant signals officer. I never heard of anything happening at Jutland of the sort that you suggest. I think that it is most improbable. Sammy was not that kind of man.

Nor was he the sort of man about whom anecdotes collect. I remember him as the gentlest of souls, very reticent, with a wonderful sense of humour—but don't ask me what we laughed about.

I think that you will find the material that you need in his work in the East End, after he retired from the Navy. From the service point of view, though a distinguished officer, he did nothing which would justify a biography.

Sorry not to be more helpful. But, though I have the most vivid recollection of Sammy as a person, I cannot remember his ever saying or doing anything out of the ordinary.

It is news to me that there was anything wrong with his legs. He rowed well and played a good game of golf. He had, now that you mention it, a rather odd way of walking, but nothing that one could regard as a disability.

Good luck to the book,

Yours, etc.,

One of the exceptions was a man whose picture of Sammy Woods tallied with the rest, but who added: "Sammy had a great reverence for authority, which I didn't, being Irish. So we did not have much in common."

The second was an admiral, who had been born in Gosport, and had known Alex intimately from his boyhood onwards. He said that he had a great deal of information about Alex, but he had heard that there was

EC—F

a possibility that a film might be made out of Alex's life, and out of loyalty to his old friend he would tell me nothing. I wrote to him twice at great length, but failed to convince him of my sincerity. It occurred to me as possible that the admiral, reflecting on the long years of his intimacy, might have discovered that after all he knew very little about Alex, though he had told Alex quite a lot about himself. That certainly was the case with Alex's other intimate friends. He received confidences but did not give them.

The third was the Navigation Officer on H.M.S. *Topaze* at the time that Alex took over command. His letter, the longest, the best written and most factual of all I received, was highly critical of Alex as a navigator and a commander of men. If only half the others were as well informed, how easy it would have been to reconstruct the detail of Alex's naval career!

But the more I cast around, the more convinced I became that my correspondents were right and it was not his naval career which was important. At the time Alex joined the Navy it was going through a period of rapid change, presided over by "Jacky" Fisher at the Admiralty. Fisher was the father of the *Dreadnought*, the first battle-ship to solve the problem of steam. At the same time Percy Scott, that rebellious and inventive genius, was tackling the problems of gunnery on a realistic basis. The obstacles he encountered were of a type which now appears to us fantastic. For example, the Captain of each ship was responsible for the appearance of his ship. He had to find the money for repainting his ship out of his own pocket. He frowned on gunnery practice because the blast from the guns blistered the paint work. His chief concern was to fire off the annual allotment of rounds in one practice without much regard for the accuracy of the shooting and then repaint so that his ship could be smart for another twelvemonth. Percy Scott's insistence that the purpose of a gun was to hit its target was the enunciation of a first principle which most captains preferred to forget.

Gradually Scott broke down the prejudices (which were exacerbated in many cases by his refusal to suffer fools gladly) and naval gunnery became more accurate at 10,000 yards than it had been previously at a thousand yards. Lively minds were at work on new means of signalling. Percy Scott was pointing out the impossibility of communication if the smokestack was placed in front of the bridge. Experiments were being carried out in signalling over the horizon by flashing searchlights on clouds. A scheme was put up for transmitting signals through water instead of air. It was never adopted but it foreshadowed the later development of Asdic. Another ingenious suggestion was to transmit morse messages in ultra-violet rays within a constant beam of light.

More important than any of these was the development of Wireless Telegraphy and the elaboration of codes and ciphers which it made necessary.

Alex was one of the last signals officers to qualify without taking W/T as part of his course. He passed brilliantly, his lowest mark being 91 per cent. He came out first with 309 marks, his runner-up having only 217. Before he joined Rear-Admiral Bridgeman, he underwent a W/T course. But he was never a technical officer in the modern sense, or what in his own day was contemptuously described as "a nuts and bolts man". He was a fine officer in a tradition flourishing in the youth of Dr Woods, but already becoming obsolescent in the first decade of this century, a tradition which valued character higher than it valued scientific knowledge. Today the ordinary non-technical officer has to be much more highly trained than Alex was when he passed out as one of the finest signals officers of his generation.

Alex had no contribution to make to the development

of naval signalling. He had neither the training nor the temperament. Technical advance is made by intellectual rebels, awkward, critical people who are constantly finding fault with their environment and looking for ways to improve it. Alex was a conformist. All his energies went to making the best use of what he was given. He was far too modest to challenge the Lords of the Admiralty. He left it to them and the Percy Scotts to fight out between them what should be done.

What I discovered about this early stage of Alex's naval career added nothing new. As a sub-lieutenant he was very kind to midshipmen at a time when many sub-lieutenants were bullies. Seeing a man late back from shore leave and in consequence liable to a charge, he took a boat and brought him aboard without the officer on duty seeing him. He had a great solicitude for the ratings under him and was most attentive to their welfare. He sought out those in the ship who were Christians and whatever their rank would have them frequently in his cabin. He was regular in his church attendance. He hated swearing and people were careful of what they said in his presence, not because they thought there was anything wrong in swearing but because they did not like to cause him pain. He was a good oarsman and he played golf for the Navy against the Army at Portsmouth. He was a rotten rider, and on parade in Malta he could not obey his commanding officer's orders because he was unable to transmit them to his horse. His sense of humour delighted in presenting himself as ridiculous.

He was very good-looking, but he was shy of women. When he was at the Sailors' Home he used to visit the Greenwich Naval Hospital and was fond of saying that he had fallen in love with one of the nurses there. It must have been when he was taking his general course at the Royal Naval College, Greenwich, at the age of nineteen. I don't think that it was very serious.

When he came back from Malta in December 1904, preparatory to taking his signals course at Portsmouth, something much more serious happened. To make this intelligible, it is necessary to sketch in what he found on his return.

Uncle Llewellyn had left by this time, but Mrs Kennedy was still there. She had been born in 1815, the year of the Battle of Waterloo, but in 1904 on the threshold of ninety she was still going strong, a bit deafer but not so deaf that she couldn't have one or other of her light novels shouted at her, a bit blinder but not so blind that she couldn't see anything she wasn't supposed to see. The walls of memory had collapsed and she sometimes grew angry when her daughter could not remember the events of 1825.

Alex's mother herself was in poor shape. When she was not being poisoned by her primulas, she was often confined to bed with bronchial complaints for weeks on end.

Dr Woods had retired for good. On the death of Queen Victoria, the Admiralty had been forced to retire him once as the only means of prising him out of the Royal Yacht. When they had hinted that it was time to go, he had answered that he thought King Edward would prefer him to stay and he was deeply aggrieved at the speed with which his successor finally relieved him of his post. After a period on half-pay, he had been recalled to the Admiralty to organize an emergency hospital and nursing scheme which could go into operation in the event of war. This job done, he was retired once more. He was miserable and casting around for some outlet for his still abundant energy, he found it in the scandal of the Alverstoke sewage effluent. He spent his days sniffing what he variously described as the aroma, stench and even on warm days with the southerly breeze the stink. He canvassed his friends for their observations where it smelt worst in what winds. Alex remained his favourite diary topic, but the sewage effluent ran him a close second. He was happiest when he combined the two, walking with Alex stink hunting.

Alex's brothers were away from home. Charles and Hugh were in India, Arthur still seeking his fortune in Canada. Charles was married to an English girl called Dorothy. Arthur had married a Canadian whom the family had never met.

Edyth and Kathleen were still at home, still spinsters. Some years before Edyth had met a friend of Charles, a brother officer in the South Lancashires. John Smith, as I shall call him, was handsome, charming, generous and possessed of a private income which brought him in about £300 a year, which in those days was worth the equivalent of £1,500 a year today. He fell in love with Edyth, who resembled her mother as a young girl. She had the same long, thin nose, the same fine black hair, the same gentleness, devotion, loyalty and lack of fighting spirit. John Smith proposed and Edyth accepted him.

John Smith was not an evil man, but his small private income gave him illusions of great wealth. If he wanted a new cricket bat, he ordered three from Wisden's, chose the one he preferred and gave the other two away. In the mess he was the centre of a school, buying more than his fair share of drinks because he had means. His money went not in debauchery and drunken excesses. It seeped slowly away in a continuous dissipation. Every day he spent and drank just a little more than he should. Yet he was very well liked by his fellow subalterns and field officers, because he was a good soldier.

John Smith ran up a few hundred pounds of debts in the South Lancashires. He paid them by transferring to a Yorkshire regiment and taking the place of an officer who had been drafted, but did not want to go, to India.

In India the same thing happened. The only way of paying his debts was to retire and commute his pension for a capital sum. With what was left of this, he went to stay with the Woods at Alverstoke.

Having given her pledge Edyth stayed grimly loyal. She attributed the failure of her fiancé not to weakness of character but to "the Drink". It was her duty to help him fight it. But it had been understood from the beginning that they should not marry until things had improved, and things had grown steadily worse since their engagement.

John Smith had twelve hundred pounds left after paying his debts. Dr Woods urged him to invest in gilt-edged. But John Smith was not interested in the yield of Consols. He wanted a handsome return for his money and he found what he wanted in the pages of *The Times*, where a financial genius was offering three-and-a-half per cent per month, guaranteed.

Dr Woods told him not to be an ass. But John Smith persisted and removed to a pub in Gosport, handy for seeing Edyth during the day and for drinking during the evening. At the end of the first month he flourished a cheque for forty guineas with a great triumph.

But no cheque came at the end of the second month and John Smith who had been drinking heavily because he was so rich began to drink more heavily still because he had been so bitterly betrayed. He could not bear to see Dr Woods, because he had been so right, or Edyth, because she did not complain. He packed his bags and shipped to Canada, hoping like Arthur Woods to find a fortune there. Before he had time to be convinced of failure, he died of cancer of the lung.

This abortive romance had taken some ten years of Edyth's life. She had been a beautiful girl when it started. By its end she was reconciled to middle age, her neck swollen with incipient goitre, her eyesight failing, her beauty gone. Grimly she gave to God the devotion which no man would want from her. Her sad soul preferred the contemplation of Christ's Passion to the glory of His love.

Her sister Kathleen took physically after her father. She was far more robust in spirit. No less religious, she found Joy in God. It was she and not Edyth who joined the Band of Hope, that association of optimists who hoped to scare people into total abstinence by exhibiting lantern slides of cirrhotic livers, tinted like bruises. She also had been engaged. It had ended not in a protracted disillusion but in tragedy. Her future husband had been drowned in a submarine disaster. But she was not broken by grief as her sister had been. Her energies found outlet in good works, in whose commission she was not merely untiring but also happy.

This was the home to which Alex returned in December 1905, an ageing and rather sad *ménage* on which his youth, his handsomeness and hopes must have burst like sunshine after a bleak winter.

Alex's delight in being back at Alverstoke after three-and-a-half years in the Mediterranean was intoxicating. He wanted to look up all his old friends to find out whether they had changed as much as he had in the years during which he had been away.

That was his first desire, but it was soon superseded by another. There was a group of young men and women who regarded themselves as "a set". There was Muriel Roxby, for example, the daughter of the Captain of the *Victoria and Albert*; there were the Blake boys, the sons of a local brewer, one of whom ended up as Vice-Admiral Sir Geoffrey Blake, K.C.B., D.S.O., a Lord Commissioner of the Admiralty and additional Assistant Chief of Naval Staff. To that set was a recent addition, a beautiful and high-spirited young girl of nineteen called Phyllis Sealey.

Her parents were living in a large rented house called Privett Lodge while they were looking for a suitable house to buy. The father, Colonel Sealey, was a gentle creature in his early sixties, who had been recently retired from India, where he had been a senior political officer. His wife was twenty years younger than he was. When she was her daughter's age, she had arrived at Aden in search of a husband. She had chosen Sealey, who was in command of the garrison and the most eligible bachelor there. Ambitious, good-looking, dominating, she had found in India the luxury, the admiration and the power which she craved. Though never actually unfaithful, she liked to have a following, in her daughter's words "*une allumineuse*".

If she had married a younger man she would have had to postpone her enjoyments. As it was, she found that at forty, when she was at the height of her powers, she was driven into retirement with her husband. She was clearly an intensely unhappy woman, so bedazzled with the lost grandeur of her official position in India as to be incapable of relishing any of the modest delights of Alverstoke.

While the Sealeys were in India, Phyllis had been educated in Europe. She had been to school in Belgium and in Germany. She had mastered French and German and conceived the ambition of becoming a concert pianist.

Her mother had other plans for her. Playing the piano was a graceful accomplishment for a gentlewoman, provided that she did not play embarrassingly well. But becoming a concert pianist, performing for money, was degrading and would unfit Phyllis for the good match which her education, beauty and parents' position could command. She was nineteen. It was high time she married. Things should be easier for Phyllis than they had been for her mother. There were so many more eligible officers at Portsmouth than there had been at Aden, and with higher ranks.

Phyllis Sealey and Alex Woods quickly fell in love. It

was a boy and girl love. With her continental education Phyllis was in some ways older than most English girls. But she was still only a girl and Alex was an inexperienced twenty-four. He nicknamed her Kiddie; but in many ways she was more knowledgeable than he was. Alex had inherited from his father a distrust of the Church of Rome and of all forms of High Anglicanism which smacked of Papacy. The Low Church of England taught the true path to God. Phyllis had worshipped in Roman Catholic churches and she did not accept the view that Roman Catholics were all benighted idolaters. Nor was she as convinced as Alex that the British way of life was superior in all respects. There were things they ordered better in France and Germany. She urged Alex to study European languages, pointing out that if he qualified as an interpreter he would get an extra allowance.

She broadened his mind, while he intensified her belief. Her religion had been a conventional Christianity, his was a vivid love of God, such as she had never met in a person of her own age.

It was a very innocent love affair. They moved with the set. They played tennis with them, at which Phyllis shone and Alex was rotten; and they played golf at which Alex excelled and Phyllis blundered. Alex bought a bicycle and every Sunday evening they would go out to a country church for evensong. There seems to have been no open lovemaking; it was just a delight in one another's company.

They were seldom alone. It was still the age of the chaperon, when it was imagined that there was only one thing which a young man and woman could do if left alone together. When they were not with the set, Alex and Phyllis were accompanied by Kathleen, who was as romantically in favour of the match as Edyth was disapproving.

Dr Woods did not confide his views to his diary, but he

noted more and more frequently that "P. Sealy" (he never mastered the spelling of the name) had been to tea, luncheon or even breakfast.

Being in love did not make Alex lazy. He started to work on signals before his leave had expired and when he became secretly engaged to Phyllis, he merely redoubled his efforts. The prospect of marriage was an incentive to do his best so that he might the sooner be in a position to marry her. He welcomed her going to the dances given in honour of the French Fleet, taking another man as partner so that he could devote the evening to work.

Some people are distracted by love. They become so turned towards the object of their love that it seems a waste of time to think of anything else. Others have their senses sharpened and their energies redoubled. The form which Alex had shown at the *Britannia* was good, but at the School of Signals it glowed into brilliance. There is no doubt that this came as an accession of power through loving and knowing that he was loved in return.

The success in his examination marked him out for a flag lieutenancy. If he had passed with lower marks, he would have soon been posted to a smaller ship as lieutenant in charge of signals. But flag lieutenants were not required every day. To fill in his waiting time, he applied for and was granted permission to go to Dieppe to study for a French interpreter's certificate. It meant separation from Phyllis, but the act itself was a tribute to her influence; and if he passed, he would be a shilling a day nearer to being able to marry her.

Dr and Mrs Woods were informed of the secret engagement and they raised no objection. Mrs Sealey laughed at the idea and refused even to discuss it. She had no objection to Alex Woods as a person. But he had no money of his own and however brilliant he might be, it would be many years before he was in the position to support a wife in the comfort which Phyllis had every right to expect.

She said no more, because she had at last found a suitable house in the charming but remote Hampshire village of Hambledon. It was eight miles from the nearest railway station and fifteen miles from Alverstoke. Distance, in her opinion, could prove a more persuasive argument than any she might put forward at this time. The removal took place before Alex left for Dieppe and it provided a sufficient obstacle for the moment.

Phyllis was forbidden to receive letters from Alex, but she made the cook, Ada, privy to her romance and every morning Ada would race to the front door the instant she heard the postman's knock and if there was any letter for Phyllis she would hide it away for secret delivery later.

Employing one of those transparent lovers' ruses that fool no one, they pretended that Phyllis was no longer interested in Alex but had formed a deep friendship for Kathleen. She begged her mother for permission to have Kathleen over to stay at Hambledon. What more natural than that Kathleen should ask Phyllis for a return visit? Mrs Sealey was content to appear to be tricked. Her daughter had something of her own determination and needed to be handled carefully. What did it matter if when Alex returned from Dieppe for Christmas, Phyllis slipped over to Alverstoke to see him? He would be back in Dieppe on Boxing Day to complete his four-month course in French.

But before the four months elapsed, a letter arrived for Alex from Captain Craddock. Alex had served under him in the Mediterranean and in accordance with his policy of following his son's interest, Dr Woods had sent him a piece of wood from the old yacht *Victoria and Albert* with the hope that Alex was shaping well. He had received a letter in reply, saying, "The Admiral considers him one of the best officers on board and always selects him for any special work. He is a great friend of mine as I think he is of everyone on board."

Dr Woods opened the letter from Craddock, though it was addressed to Alex. It contained the news that Rear-Admiral Francis Bridgeman wanted Alex as his Flag Lieutenant. The Doctor re-sealed the letter and sent it on to Alex in Dieppe by the late-night post. With a dispatch that could not be emulated by the Anglo-French postal services half a century later, it was delivered early next morning. Alex packed his things immediately, caught the next boat to England and rang his father from London that evening.

Reporting next morning at the Admiralty, he learnt that the flagship, H.M.S. *Venerable*, would be returning on Admiral's leave from the Mediterranean in three weeks' time. If he accepted the appointment, he would be gazetted on Monday, 5 March, in three days' time, and should report to the Signal School in Portsmouth for a W/T course, which would keep him occupied until it was time for him to join the *Venerable*.

Alex accepted with alacrity. It was exactly the sort of opening for which he had been working. He saw the future opening brightly for Phyllis and himself. He hurried down to Alverstoke and broke the news to the family and to Phyllis.

The family was overjoyed, but Phyllis looked depressed. The last time he had been posted to the Mediterranean he had stayed away three-and-a-half years. The thought of a three-year separation appalled her. At nineteen, the only way you can measure three years in the immediate future is to estimate how you have changed in the last three years. At nineteen, Phyllis could not feel any sense of identity with the child she had been at sixteen. What sort of a person would she be at twenty-two?

Alex was loving and reassuring. But he did not carry much conviction with Phyllis. His was a constant character. He had always been very much the same person, whatever his age. She was volatile and certain only that there were many different people she was capable of becoming, depending upon what happened to her and especially upon whom she married. Besides it would be far easier for Alex to be constant, cooped up for the most part in a ship and with constant work to do, than it would be for her, engaged but at the same time not engaged, stuck away in her mother's house at Hambledon, subject day in and day out to lectures on the necessity of making a good match. She would have found it easy enough to wait three years or more for Alex, if she had seen him from time to time during that period, growing up with him. It was the separation which she feared with the letter-post their only link and Alex the least communicative of letter-writers.

Malta is so few hours from London today that when the Queen Mother went down to St Paul's, Dock Street to unveil the memorial window to Alex, his nephew Guy flew back for the ceremony. If it had been necessary he could have been back on parade first thing the next morning.

It is hard to think ourselves back to 1906 estimates of distance. In those days Malta was a long way for civilians, who could move as and when they wished. For service personnel who stayed with a ship for the length of its commission, usually three years, Malta was as far from Portsmouth as the South Pole.

Alex's attempts to comfort her were not successful. She wanted something more than his distant constancy, a regularization of her position. If only her engagement could be announced!

While Alex was still at Portsmouth, Mrs Sealey temporized. She was afraid that if she disclosed her opposition, Phyllis might commit the folly of getting married secretly. She waited until the *Venerable* sailed and then she told her daughter to put all this nonsense out of her head. Alex was a likeable enough young man but totally unsuitable as a husband. She would under no circumstances allow the engagement to be announced. It was not enough for Phyllis to say that she considered herself engaged to be married to Alex. Her mother continued to treat her as a young girl whose affections were unattached, introducing her to eligible young bachelors and not so young but even more eligible bachelors, and behaving altogether with the licence of a mother whose daughter was on offer in the marriage market.

Phyllis was placed in an awkward position. There was one code of behaviour accepted towards young women engaged to be married and another, more gallant and flirtatious, towards the fancy-free. By the same token, after she had pledged her troth, a young lady had to conduct herself with a gravity which in an unattached spinster would have been regarded as an unwarrantable stiffness, an unbecoming frigidity.

How was Phyllis Sealey to behave? If she acted as was becoming to Alex's *fiancée*, everybody would think her cold, ungracious, utterly changed from the vivacious and charming girl she had been. Yet if she stayed her gay old self, she would be doubly guilty. She would be acting unfaithfully to Alex and misleading the suitors whom her mother was lining up.

There was no appeal to Colonel Sealey. His talents had been devoted to the administration of the Indian empire; his home and family were the province of his wife. He loved his daughter but he would never have dared to intervene against his wife.

Phyllis was forced to fight alone, her only allies being Kathleen in Alverstoke and Ada in the kitchen, who continued to bring her surreptitiously the letters which were such a poor substitute for Alex's presence.

How long the family warfare lasted I cannot discover. A very long time, it seems to Phyllis in retrospect. But memory is notoriously inaccurate in such matters, especially after the lapse of more than half a century. What remains vivid is the final battle.

It began with Phyllis raising once more the announcement of her engagement to Alex.

There followed a scene which her mother had perhaps rehearsed many times. "You will not announce your engagement to that young man now or ever," she said. "As your mother I should consider it a dereliction of my duty ever to consent to such a wildly unsuitable marriage." Her objection, repeated many times in different ways, was simply that Alex could neither inherit nor for many years earn for himself enough money to support Phyllis in the way she had been brought up to live. "He may be a brilliant flag lieutenant," she said, "but he can't even afford to buy a bicycle outright. It may appear very romantic to you now. But you expect a certain standard of comfort, of pleasant clothes, without having to worry about each penny you have to spend. Look at poor Mrs Woods, a chronic invalid. Six children one after the other. Having to bring them up on a service pittance. No wonder her health broke down. And do you see yourself the mother of another six? You can be quite sure a pious young man like Alex won't believe in any limitation of the family."

Some of the things which Mrs Sealey said, if they were not true, at least coincided with her basest fears. On both sides the argument grew violent. The hatred which mother and daughter had come to feel for one another was more openly expressed than it had ever been before. Both of them were appalled at what they were saying, but neither of them could stop.

The scene ended with Mrs Sealey stalking out of the room. But the drama was not over. She went out to the kitchen and gave Ada a verbatim account of what had happened, leaving the doors open so that her daughter could hear and adding a commentary on how the manners of children had degenerated since she was a girl. I suspect that though she had lost control of her temper, she knew that here was her chance to turn her initial advantage into a rout.

Ada was filled with shame at having to listen to this denunciation of Miss Phyllis. But there was no means for a servant to stop her mistress making a degrading scene and Phyllis considered it beneath her dignity to interrupt. She stayed where she was, listening to every word and vowing that she would get away from her mother the moment she could.

The drama moved into its third scene when Mrs Sealey returned to say how disgusted Ada was to hear how she had behaved to her mother. Ada had never heard of a daughter speaking to her mother in such a way.

"Don't worry. I shan't speak to you in any way much longer," Phyllis said. "I've made up my mind to marry the first man who proposes to me, merely to get away from this horrible, horrible house."

Ada came later to Phyllis to apologize for having had to listen to Mrs Sealey's tirade. When Phyllis told her of her resolve, she was appalled. She begged her to be calm, to remember that Alex loved her, to do nothing rash out of anger or hatred.

But Mrs Sealey did not relax her advantage. She told herself that she was far too good a mother to care whether it was spite or hatred which drove her daughter to make a good match, so long as the match was good. She dropped a note to her favourite suitor, who had already proposed once and been turned down. A second attempt, she hinted, might meet with more success.

It did.

Phyllis's motives must have been an extraordinary tangle. She wanted to get away from home at any price. There was perhaps just a possibility that her mother was right and she wrong. If so, the choice of her mother's candidate would bring a reconciliation. But if her mother was wrong, Phyllis would be able to hold it against her for the rest of her life. And to have just cause for hating her mother at that moment was more important than to marry the man she loved, or thought she loved, years hence.

If Alex had been stationed at Portsmouth, he could have bicycled over and given her the faith which he had in love without any of this nonsense about becoming exhausted by childbearing and living in the starkest poverty. But Alex was in Malta and the letter which she wrote to him was not an appeal for help. It was the announcement of her engagement.

He wrote back regretfully accepting her decision. But after that the correspondence lapsed.

At this point in her story, I asked Phyllis how long after Alex's departure she made this decision to marry a man she did not love, in order to leave home.

"I can't remember," she said. "It was a most terrible mistake. I would never have made it if Alex had not been in Malta those three years. The actual marriage was 1907, I suppose, or 1908. At any rate it was before Alex got back."

As the reader may have noticed, Alex did not spend three years in the Mediterranean under Bridgeman. He returned with him a year less a day after he had left. It was the *prospect* of a three-year wait that broke Phyllis down and not the reality.

Almost immediately after her marriage, she sailed to India with her husband's regiment. The marriage was a ghastly failure. Temperamentally they were completely unsuited. "He lay on a hard board at night and practised Yoga and I couldn't stand it," she said, "so I ran away and got an annulment by Scottish law after three years."

After the annulment Phyllis met Alex again. They got

on wonderfully with one another. There was no question of marriage. According to Scottish law she might be free, but according to Alex's belief she was still married and he could never marry her.

Phyllis did marry a second time and she had a number of children, to the eldest of whom Alex acted as god-father. It was when they were coming away from the confirmation of this child that he said to Phyllis, "You know you are the only woman I have ever loved."

Phyllis was very happy in her second marriage and in her children. But in her seventies she looks back and says, "I still think what a terrible mistake I made in not marrying Alex. It is something I have always regretted."

I have told this story as I have pieced it together from different sources. It interested me because of its inevitable unhappiness. When one takes into account the main characters, the handsome penurious Alex, the ambitious mother and the daughter torn between the two, one feels that it could not have happened in any other way.

Yet it is only satisfying if one has a very mordant humour. All the characters fail in what they will. Alex loses his girl, Mrs Sealey fails to secure the good match which she wants for her daughter and Phyllis loses the man she loves and ends up by hating herself more than her mother for the marriage of spite.

That was the interpretation which I put on it. But at the same time this was a situation which could be examined in the light of Howard Marshall's thesis that it might be possible to see the hand of God at work at certain periods of Alex's life to turn Alex from what he thought was good for himself to what in fact was better.

Suppose that Phyllis had stood up to her mother's taunts and her separation from Alex. Suppose that they had married. What would have happened?

There would have been a number of children. Some

of them would have inherited muscular atrophy from Alex. The love between the two of them would, I am sure, have been able to survive the shock of discovering this. But it would have been an agony for the parents and the affected children to decide whether to take the risk of transmitting it to another generation. The marriage would not have been as untainted by sorrow as Phyllis had always dreamed it would have been.

Alex would have become a family man, as devoted and loving a father to his children as Dr Woods had been to him. His love would have been centred on a few people, and after leaving the Royal Navy he might well have accepted the job of organizing the work of the Society for the Propagation of the Gospel in East Anglia, which he passed on to his brother Hugh. There would never have been an East End phase, in which he was available to help any bum who came to him in distress. He would have died a good and pious man, but his opportunity for sainthood would have been missed.

Phyllis Sealey probably derived more good from Alex by regarding him as the man whom if she had been true to herself she would have married than she would have done if she had married him and found that he had brought a hereditary taint into her family.

It was possible, therefore, if you believed as Howard Marshall and Alex Woods did in a Divine Purpose greater and wiser than that of human beings, to see this frustration of Alex's love for Phyllis Sealey as a beneficent intervention by God. It made sense of what was otherwise cruel nonsense.

In Kathleen also the signs of progressive muscular atrophy were apparent before she died. For her too, it might be argued, that it was providential that her *fiancé* was drowned. She was spared the sorrow of having children who might have been denied the delight of marriage in their turn.

But what about Edyth and John Smith? It was not so easy to see any explanation for her. She was stricken with glaucoma so that there was only one small patch of vision left, by which she could see to walk but little more. But she lived to a ripe age. There was no sign of muscular atrophy. Her children would have been free.

But would her life have been fuller married to John Smith? Wouldn't he have dragged her through a series of degradations compared to which her sad fixation on God's sorrows was a form of paradise?

It was difficult to decide about Edyth. I could imagine Howard Marshall saying, "You can't expect to see the Hand of God everywhere, my dear fellow. Think how lucky you are to detect it in the lives of Alex and Kathleen. And anyway, how do you know that Edyth didn't come nearer to God through losing that drunkard Smith than she would ever have done waiting up for him night after night?"

It was the infuriating thing about Christians. If their God existed, everything was possible.

CHAPTER SEVEN

FROM the time that Alex joined Rear-Admiral Bridgeman as Flag Lieutenant until the outbreak of the First World War, his career followed the copybook. His only deviation from the norm was that he was far more religious than most officers and that his loyalties as a Christian cut across the accepted distinctions of rank. He made friends with all his fellow-Christians irrespective of their rank. If he had been an officer responsible for discipline, this would have provoked conflict and criticism. But the Admiral's staff on a flagship is a community within a community and the Flag Lieutenant is a technical officer when he is on duty, and off-duty is almost as free to range as the ship's chaplain.

The only significant development during this period seems to have been his turning to ritualism. As one would expect, it was not the result of study or intellectual argument.

When Charles returned to England with his wife and son, Dorothy started to go to a church called All Saints, an Italianate red-brick building in the style of St Mark's Venice, on the borders of Gosport and Haslar. She found the services, in her own words, "nicer than those in the Alverstoke parish church". Charles and Edyth accompanied her and they agreed. Alex went there when he was on leave and he too found something which had been lacking in the Low Church services to which he was accustomed.

All Saints was not the sort of church which is known as

"spiky", more Roman than the Romans, with thurifers and acolytes and the Mass so gabbled that for all anyone could hear it might be in Latin. Its services were in the tradition of the Tractarian Movement, with emphasis on Holy Communion rather than Mattins and Evensong, and on worship rather than sermons. The Host was reserved for adoration. Round the church were the Stations of the Cross. There were the vestments and candles of which Queen Victoria and Dr Woods disapproved. There was voluntary confession.

Alex at this time disapproved of confession for the usual Low Church reasons. But the ritual appealed to him. There was a great deal of ritual in the Royal Navy from the piping aboard of the admiral to the saluting of officers. Why shouldn't the service of God be as rich as the service of the King and Queen? If the Royal Navy had its ceremonial uniforms, why should not the priesthood? In neither case were they objects of personal grandeur; they were symbols of respect, a form of tribute to the master served.

As a signals officer Alex dealt almost entirely in symbols. Flags, lights, morse, codes and ciphers were all part of the apparatus of conveying meaning through symbolism. The use of symbols in Holy Worship in consequence appeared to him not a form of mumbo-jumbo as it did to his father, but a language capable of sustaining meanings difficult to frame in words. He found beauty in the idea that the flames of candles should carry prayers towards heaven.

His private life was not aesthetic. He did not respond to the beauties of literature, music or the visual arts. The rituals of the Royal Navy and the Anglo-Catholic Church helped to make up this lack.

Knowing that when he was in the East End, he was fond of giving his communicants little books on the seventeenth-century Bishop Lancelot Andrewes, the father of the Anglo-Catholic Church, I asked Dorothy Woods when he had first come across Lancelot Andrewes. She looked puzzled and said, "I didn't know he'd ever met him. He never mentioned him to me." When I explained, she said that his favourite Anglo-Catholic writer had been Bishop Gore.

Whatever he may have read, theory came after practice. It gave content to a belief already accepted.

Hitherto I have been showing the extent to which Alex derived from his father. Alex's acceptance of Anglo-Catholicism is the first indication of his making decisions in contradiction to his father. The Doctor regarded the Tractarians as a sort of Fifth Column within the Church of England, traitors who would lead the Anglicans back to Rome. It must have come as a shock to him that three of his children should have repudiated that view. But perhaps by that time he had modified his opinions. They had been an echo of Queen Victoria's and he respected his children too much to abominate their beliefs, even if he did not agree with them.

I think it possible that Phyllis Sealey had widened Alex's view and prepared him for the acceptance of a sacramental religion by her defence of Roman Catholicism on the continent. It is certain that he must have entered Catholic churches in Dieppe, l'Eglise de St Jacques, for example, and l'Eglise de St Remy, and it is probable that he worshipped in them. All Saints, Gosport, gave him what he may have been looking for since then, services which were English and yet had the colour and richness of Catholicism.

Yet though Alex became an Anglo-Catholic, he was never a sectarian. There were many paths to God. He was satisfied with trying to find the one which was right for himself, without trying to bar all other ways. As he wrote to Lettice, he had a respect for the sincere Low Churchman. At the outbreak of the First World War he met the man whom he grew to admire more than any other man living, Admiral John Jellicoe: an intensely religious man and a Low Churchman.

Jellicoe embodied all the qualities which Alex admired and strove to emulate. He was quiet, cautious and undramatic, supremely good at his job, undeflected from what he considered his duty by the agitation of the Press, the temptation of the grand gesture or the pressure of politicians. His judgment was so balanced that he could resist the temptation of a small spectacular triumph which might put his supreme task of safeguarding Britain and her supply-routes in jeopardy. His modesty was founded not on diffidence but on his belief that only with God's help could a man succeed and then the glory was not to the man but his Maker. Though concerned with the great issues of grand strategy, he remained solicitous of the men who served under him, demanding of them nothing that he would not do himself. This capacity for thinking himself into the minds of other people, which is one of the aspects of humility, enabled him to anticipate the tactics and strategy of the enemy more accurately than a more dashing and self-centred commander.

I would not say that Jellicoe's influence changed the direction of Alex's life in the slightest. It merely confirmed him in the rightness of his course. He must often, in the eighteen years which he had spent in the Navy before he met Jellicoe, have felt very lonely and despondent, wondering whether this attempt to combine the religious with the naval life was an utter waste of both. He had persisted with a pertinacious faith and his soul rejoiced to discover that the Admiral of the Grand Fleet had been ahead of him the whole time on the same bearing. The feeling of eccentricity which religious people experience in the darkness of the soul fell away from him. He was not a crank, an oddity. He was merely exceptionally normal.

Alex had the same quality as Jellicoe of being able to think himself into another man's position. It was this which won him the D.S.O. at the Battle of Jutland, and not any interposed message from Almighty God.

There is an exercise which they practise in the Army. A message is passed from the head of a file of men to the tail, each man turning round and repeating it to the man behind him. Very seldom does it reach the tail exactly as it was given to the head. More often than not it is mangled out of all meaning or translated into something totally different. This is funny enough on Salisbury Plain. But in action it produces the courageous folly of the charge of the Light Brigade.

At sea, clarity of signalling is even more important. One of the most famous examples of a mistaken naval signal occurred in the year before the Battle of Jutland, during the Battle of the Dogger Bank. In the later stages of that engagement, when his flagship, H.M.S. *Lion*, had been hit in fifteen places and was badly crippled, Admiral Beatty signalled his battle cruiser squadron to attack the rear of the retreating German force. The signal consisted of two flags. Compass B, which meant "Course north-east", and A.F. which meant "Attack the rear of the enemy".

H.M.S. *Lion* was listing heavily to port. All but two of her signal halyards had been shot away. When the flags were hoisted, they read as one signal, "Attack the rear of the enemy bearing north-east."

There was only one enemy bearing north-east. This was the *Blücher*, which had been badly crippled and separated from her consorts. H.M.S. *Indomitable* had been told off to give her the *coup de grâce*. But Rear-Admiral Moore took Beatty's signal to mean that he should concentrate the fire of the battle cruiser squadron on the *Blücher*. An overwhelming concentration of fire was directed against the *Blücher*, while the remaining German battle cruisers drew steadily away.

Beatty saw what was happening but he could not understand why. Furious, he ordered his flag lieutenant to hoist the famous signal which Nelson used at Trafalgar. "Engage the enemy more closely." But since that historic occasion the signal had been removed from the signal book.

The next best thing was, "Keep nearer the enemy." But by the time that was hoisted, H.M.S. *Lion* had dropped too far astern and the signal was hidden by smoke.

If Beatty's signals had been intelligible, the Battle of the Dogger Bank would have been so decisive that the Battle of Jutland would not have been fought as early as it was.

Alex did not need the Battle of the Dogger Bank to teach him clarity. He must have learnt it many times during manœuvres. But the Battle of the Dogger Bank forced it home. At Jutland he must have scrutinized every signal which he was ordered to give. "Is this crystal-clear? If not, how can it be made so?"

I don't propose to join the arguments which are still waged about the rights and wrongs of the Battle of Jutland. Alex's part as recorded by the histories was memorable for the querying of one order.

The signalling throughout the engagement was most unsatisfactory. For example, when at 6.1 p.m. on 1 May 1916 the battle cruisers under Beatty were sighted by the *Iron Duke*, Jellicoe signalled to Beatty on the *Lion*, "Where is the enemy's battlefleet?"

Five minutes passed before there was a reply, five terribly important minutes to Jellicoe, whose fleet in that time had travelled three and-a-half miles. When the reply came, it stated merely that the enemy's battle cruisers were bearing south-east, which gave no indication where the battleships of the German Grand Fleet were. The answer to the *Iron Duke's* question was not given until six-fourteen. Twenty seconds later, with no enemy in sight Jellicoe gave the order. "Hoist equal speed pendant South East."

This manœuvre, which was calculated to "cross the enemy's T" and enable the British Grand Fleet to open their broadsides on an enemy able to fire only with the fore batteries, was one which according to Jellicoe's biographer, Sir Reginald Bacon, had "rarely, if ever, been practised before by the Grand Fleet" under Jellicoe's command. It was a rare and clever manœuvre, to meet a difficult and dangerous situation.

When Alex received it as Fleet Signals Officer, he knew exactly what his Admiral wanted. But it was just possible that in the heat of battle it would be misunderstood and the deployment might be made from the starboard instead of the port division. If the mistake was made, it would give the advantage to the enemy. Though he had a great reverence for authority, Alex queried the order. If the signal was made to deploy on a south-east-by-east course, instead of south-east, it would be absolutely plain on which column the deployment was to be made.

Sir John Jellicoe agreed and at six-fifteen the coloured flags broke from the mast of the *Iron Duke* and at the same time the message went out by radio. "The die was irrevocably cast," wrote Sir Reginald Bacon, "the subsequent course of action was decided, and the Starboard Wing Division was, as a matter of fact, saved from what, in all probability, would have been annihilation if the deployment had been ordered on that Division."

Many decorations are awarded to officers in token of a unit's bravery. Alex's D.S.O. was won by his personal coolness and quick-thinking in the heat of battle. He regarded Jutland, as did many of his comrades, as the greatest moment of his career.

But as to interposed messages or reflections on his vocation as a priest, there was absolutely no evidence. Purely on the grounds that at this moment of his career he had to concentrate every particle of his being on the job in hand, the suggestion was utterly fantastic.

If I had to hazard a guess as to when he began to think that he would have to make a choice between the service of the Royal Navy or of God, I should say that it began in the autumn of 1916, when he assumed command of H.M.S. *Topaze*. Under Jellicoe, who so perfectly combined his religion and his career, Alex must have thought that he had reached a solution of his problem. He was ready for a command.

But the *Topaze* was not a flagship and Alex was not a fleet admiral cut off from the day-to-day problems of discipline and command. It was called a light armoured cruiser. It owed its existence to the fact that as soon as destroyers had been invented to cope with torpedo-boats, it was necessary to invent something slightly bigger, faster and more heavily gunned to cope with torpedo-boat destroyers. It was the largest of the small ships, lean-waisted, uncomfortable in a calm sea and hell in a rough one.

It was manned by a wartime crew, a few regulars diluted by a large draft from the Royal Naval Voluntary Reserve. The previous Captain had built up a free-and-easy wartime discipline, which was excellent of its kind. He knew he was dealing with civilians, who were keen enough to win the war and get back to Civvy Street, but impatient of spit and polish. When they were ashore, they liked to get tight. They swore like pirates. They were slack about inessentials. But they were good at fighting.

The *Topaze* was based upon Taranto and was working in liaison with the Italian fleet on patrolling the entrance to the Adriatic. It was a dull job, consisting of laying mines, ensuring that the Austrian Navy did not escape from the Adriatic, and clearing the minefields laid by the Austrians.

But the officers and crew of the *Topaze* were veterans. They had been right through the Gallipoli campaign and to them the Battle of Jutland, joined one dusk and ended the next dawn, was nothing to make a song and dance about. They had been in and out of action for weeks on end. They resented "the big ship wallahs", who hung around for months and then claimed that one engagement had changed the course of the war.

The Navigation Officer had served with Sammy Woods on the *Iron Duke* and had announced that for a big ship wallah he was all right, a bit fussy maybe to start with, but he'd shake down.

Almost any other officer coming from a flagship would have shaken down. It was the natural adjustment to a small and far more intimate community of officers and men. But Alex was filled with the sense of having at last found in Jellicoe a servant of God and their Lords Commissioners of the Admiralty. He remembered the pleasure of Winnington Ingram, the Bishop of London, at being introduced to all the Christians aboard the *Iron Duke*. His missionary fervour was high.

The whole tone of the *Topaze* was wrong. The First Lieutenant drank too much, never on duty, never so much that he was incapable, but always a little in excess, like Edyth's fiancé, John Smith. It was not good from a naval point of view. From a Christian point of view it was terrible.

Apart from his rank, Jellicoe had commanded respect from everyone by his competence. He knew what should be done better than any of his subordinates. His Christianity did not depend upon his professional brilliance, but was reinforced by it.

Alex was not in the same class. He was beginning to pay the price for his father's pulling of strings. The ability he had shown as a specialist officer had carried him to the command of the *Topaze*, but it had not provided him with the experience necessary for such a simple general command. He was too highly specialized in signals and not sufficiently experienced in other branches.

This must have happened often with other officers promoted from specialist jobs to the command of ships. And there was clearly a give and take in those other cases. The subordinate officers would take into account that they were serving under a man who had specialized as a signaller or a gunner. They would help him out, on the tacit understanding that he would help them out.

But Alex was not the normal naval officer. He was bored by bawdy stories. He was deeply pained by blasphemies which meant nothing to the men who uttered them; he turned his cabin into a sort of Chapel of Ease, with religious emblems taking the places normally occupied by bottles of gin and angostura bitters. He was more interested in life after death than he was in going on living. Cutting across the distinctions made by the Admiralty were those made by the Christian Church. A Christian stoker, his officers felt, might come closer to the Captain than an agnostic second in command. Very odd types popped into the Captain's cabin and it was difficult to know whether they were seeing him in his official rank of captain or as the senior Christian on board.

The motives of his officers and crew were very mixed and comparatively few of them felt as simply as Alex did that to fight and conquer the Germans and their Allies was the simple duty of a Christian to his king and country.

Some of them thought that he was a gentle and charming man, who should never have been put in command of a ship, the sort of crank in whom the regular Navy specialized. Others, more sophisticated, found him terribly lacking in the culture necessary in a commanding officer. His Paymaster, placed in charge of signals for the duration of the war, was very gratified that so distinguished a signals officer should approve his system, but he was appalled that Alex had no use for history.

"I don't see the point of history," Alex said; "it just seems a waste of time."

The Paymaster's love of history was as great as his captain's love of God. To him it was almost a blasphemy to hear someone discount the study of the growth of human knowledge, institutions and societies as a waste of time. He tried to represent to Alex that it was part of his duty as an officer in the Royal Navy to understand the development of the British Empire and the way of life for which the Allies were fighting. A naval officer, he argued, was the diplomatic representative of his country in every port of call. Who could respect what Great Britain stood for, if her representatives were themselves ignorant of their country's history?

Alex was unimpressed. The least intellectual of men, he felt perhaps that foreigners would judge Great Britain less by the intelligence of naval officers than by their behaviour and character. Upright conduct was more convincing than any history lesson; and the most brilliant exposition of parliamentary democracy could easily be eclipsed by a drunken sailor starting a fight in a brothel.

Alex must have been unhappy in this first command of his. In the *Iron Duke* it had been possible to reconcile the service of Jesus Christ with that of the Lords Commissioners of the Admiralty. As Captain of the *Topaze* Alex found that the tasks were in conflict with one another. The ship's complement was no more Christian than the British public as a whole. Alex antagonized at least some of his officers by his religious devotion and they were able to retaliate by emphasizing his inefficiency as an officer. He had forgotten most of what he knew of navigation and he asked his navigating officer to reduce the laws of navigation to that simple system of mnemonics known as Pelmanism, which was popular at that time.

The Navigating Officer answered tartly that anyone who tried to pelmanize a ship in the Adriatic would land it on the rocks. Before Alex's arrival the *Topaze* had been a happy ship. His assumption of command spread conflict, bad feeling and an uneasy guilt. The First Officer began to count the number of his drinks, as soon as he became aware that Alex was counting them. Drinking stopped being convivial. It became a gesture of defiance, a form of moral protest against the sober man of God, who, as the result of a single action, had been given a command over men who had been in a score of engagements.

Rather than single out the First Officer for reprimand, Alex issued the order that no officer should have more than three tots of hard liquor a day; and as a result the Bacchus party had three tots every day, whereas before there had been days when they had taken none.

One must not exaggerate. This skirmish over drinks is vivid in the memory of the Navigation Officer, who was a friend of the First Officer, but the Paymaster, himself a moderate drinker, remembers nothing of it. He remarked to me, "I don't see why the Navigation Officer should have expected Sammy Woods to be a first-class navigator. That he should want him to be seems to me to show that he had not complete confidence in his own ability."

"What did you think of Alex as a captain?" I asked.

"I sailed with him twice," the Paymaster answered, "on the *Topaze* and later on H.M.S. *Concord* where things were much easier because it was peacetime and all the the men were regulars. In neither ship was he what I would call a captain. He did not dominate the ship. In fact he might as well not have been there for any leadership he gave us. He was too gentle. He tried to put the Love of God into us, and a captain should be able to put the Fear of God into his men."

He went on to say that Alex hated being responsible for discipline. A captain should regard his ship as a whole, meting out punishment in order to maintain a healthy morale throughout. The individual should be a secondary consideration. Alex failed, in view of the Paymaster, because he paid too great a regard to the individual.

This was so vague that I asked for an example. The Paymaster instanced the case of a young sailor charged with a homosexual offence. Alex interviewed him alone in the Captain's cabin; "a highly dangerous thing to do. If the young man had been unscrupulous, he might have brought charges against Sammy. A captain should never interrogate a man about such charges except with witnesses. But Sammy was so concerned about the man's soul that he was prepared to take the risk—if indeed he ever considered that there might be a risk."

"And were there charges?"

"No. And as it happened, at the court martial the young sailor was acquitted."

It occurs to me that a captain would only be liable to charges of indecency from a rating, if the captain were in some slight degree an unconscious homosexual. There seems not the slightest trace of this aberration in Alex and it is likely that by talking to the man in private he was able to secure an assurance of his innocence which might not have been forthcoming in the presence of a witness.

Other witnesses support the evidence of the two foregoing. One officer remarks that Alex tried to run the ship as if it was a seminary and another that he would have been happier as a hermit on a raft.

But despite these criticisms he seems to have satisfied his superiors. At Taranto there was an Italian admiral spoiling to go to sea, but forbidden by his Government to risk his precious flagship by taking it out of port. Alex invited him to use the *Topaze* as his flagship. It made Alex happy to have an admiral aboard after all those years on flagships, and it made the Admiral so happy that when the *Topaze* was transferred to Aden, he recommended Alex for an Italian decoration.

When the *Topaze* was posted to the Red Sea, they spent some time looking ineffectually for the German raider *Wolf*, which was hundreds of miles away from the area they were ordered to search.

After this they were put on the Perim Patrol. "If anyone tells you that Aden is the ghastliest hole on earth," wrote one of Alex's officers, "you can be certain he has never been to Perim." Perim was an island at the bottom end of the Red Sea, with the emphasis on the word "bottom". From it the Patrol would intercept Arab dhows smuggling arms, pilgrims and hashish, or steamers which might possibly have carried saboteurs to blow up (or down) the Suez Canal installations.

It was very hot and very boring. Sometimes they grew hotter still, arguing which was greater, the heat or the boredom; then ennui intervened.

If they had been nearer the heart of the war (which was by then the Atlantic) there might have been greater enthusiasm. But the Red Sea was merely a sort of appendix, to be ignored except when inflamed. And the Turks had far too high a regard for life to waste it on operations which could not influence the final outcome of the war.

They had some shore batteries with a certain nuisance value, which they fired off more from a sense of duty than in a spirit of anger. In somewhat the same spirit operations were undertaken to silence them. This is the account, given by the Navigation Officer of an engagement very different in scale and importance from Alex's only other action, Jutland.

On Sunday, 10 June 1917, we left Aden for a rendezvous two miles west of Centre Peak Island. This was the start of the Salif Operation. The Army at Aden had been invited to form the landing party, but the G.O.C. could not give a reply without first referring the matter to Simla. The reply was anxiously awaited but never came. We delayed our departure to the last possible moment, but finally had to leave without the Army.

The *Topaze* was therefore required to provide the naval landing party under the command of Captain A. R. W. Woods. We all wondered what would happen, for at that time the Navy were not good at "playing at soldiers".

Shortly after getting clear of Aden, our speed fell away badly and the Chief reported that he could not steam with the coal we had taken on at Aden. This coal had been drawn from Admiralty stocks and had been lying in the blazing sun for months. All the combustible volatiles had therefore been volatilized and the coal was mostly slack, which with a following wind was sprayed liberally over the bridge. In order to maintain speed we had to light up all boilers and even then had difficulty in maintaining twelve knots. However, we arrived at the rendezvous in time and there met H.M.S. *Northbrook* under the command of Admiral Boyle.

At 3.30 a.m. on Tuesday, June 12, we left the anchorage off Risha Island and proceeded through Kamaran Passage and at 4.30 a.m. we stopped and lowered boats which proceeded to Salif Pier with the landing party. By 5 a.m. landing was in progress and from 5.20 to 8.30 a.m. *Topaze* was bombarding various points on the peninsula, to cover the landing party and stop artillery fire. For this purpose we steamed slowly along the coast, firing port and starboard guns alternately.

We found, however, that every time we got to the end of a run to turn round, the Turks opened fire. After having two funnel-guys shot away, one near-miss on the foretop and another on the bridge, we came to the conclusion it was better not to turn round but to keep moving; so we carried out the runs, going ahead and astern alternately and firing the port guns only. After adopting this method, all Turkish shells went very wide. At 8.30 a.m. we ceased fire and at 8.40 a.m. the garrison surrendered.

During the forenoon the landing party was re-embarked with between seventy and eighty Turkish prisoners. They camped out on the poop and seemed a friendly lot of people, though in appearance villainous. Early in the afternoon *Northbrook* grounded and we were ordered to tow her off. We towed her clear at 3.30 and at 3.50 p.m. we anchored off Salif. The only casualty during the action ashore happened to my Marine servant, Private Jarman, and he got a bullet-wound in the behind. It was only a flesh-wound and it healed up quickly.

At 5.30 p.m. on Wednesday, 13 June, we arrived back at Aden, and as we came up the swept channel we received a signal from the Army asking whether it was too late. Simla's approval had been received.

In speaking of "one casualty", the First Officer was referring only to the *Topaze*. The citation to the bar to Alex's D.S.O. in the *London Gazette* of 1 August 1917 read: "Salif was attacked at dawn and captured after a three hours' resistance at the cost of only two casualties to the attacking force. This was largely due to the skilful manner in which Commander Woods conducted the advance." The second casualty of the action was Private Charles H. Read, R.M.L.I., of H.M.S. *Odin*. He was killed and Alex kept a snapshot of the cross marking his grave.

Early in 1918 the monotony of the Perim Patrol was broken by an assignment to escort some transports carrying German East African prisoners from Perim to Suez; and shortly after orders came to pay off at Suez. Alex was to remain in command but he had a new wardroom of officers, who accepted him as the boss without any odious comparison with a predecessor.

The feeling of rancour disappeared from the *Topaze*, but the estimates of his character were much the same. Lieutenant (now Vice-Admiral) H. J. Egerton, who superseded the previous Navigation Officer, remarks, "I have a feeling that he was probably happier in a staff appointment than in an independent command. I am sure he hated seeing defaulters and having to punish anybody." "Just a quiet, kind little man," said a reservist who later became a doctor, "obviously out of his element in the rough-and-tumble of sea life." The new Engineer, Lieutenant-Commander H. E. Brook, was a Christian and he liked and admired Alex very much. He remembers climbing the peak at Aden with Alex, a friend from the Aden Bank and the new Paymaster.

It was not a hard climb but stiff going. Selfishly I only thought of getting to the top first. The Bank man was soon after me. Woods and the Pay arrived a long time after. Woods had spotted that the Pay was one of those people who can't stand heights and stayed with him and coaxed and guided him up.

I have no doubt that Alex did steer the Pay up the Peak. But he could never have taken part in a race to the top. He was beginning to feel that there was something wrong with his legs, something more than a "natural grogginess". But he spoke of it to no one. So long as he could get by without inefficiency or detection there was no need to bother. He succeeded so well that none of the officers or men under him realized that there was anything wrong with his legs.

There was far more to worry the P.M.O. than the Captain's legs. Within eight days of the signature of the Armistice, Aden was struck by the influenza epidemic which in four months was to kill more people than the four years of the bloodiest war in history.

It started in a small way, eight ratings reporting sick, pains in the head and joints. That was 19 November. Next day there were only four. But there were other ships reporting sickness, and ashore also. On the fourth day there were twenty-five new cases, on the fifth, thirty-one, on the seventh—the worst day of all—there were sixty-six. They got beyond the routine sick parades morning and evening. The men and officers would keel over and report sick. A barracks was commandeered as an emergecny hospital for the less serious cases and every hour or so a new batch would be sent ashore.

There were two hundred and twenty-two cases in all

aboard the *Topaze*, but there was only one death. Alex did not go down. He was assiduous in visiting the sick in hospital and barracks. Perhaps the sense of responsibility gave him a heightened resistance. It sometimes does.

It had not done so in the case of his sister Kathleen. The epidemic had struck Alverstoke in October and Kathleen, who was a V.A.D., went down with a cold after working all night in the hospital. That was 23 October. Edyth retired to bed the same day, then the new maid, then the Doctor himself.

All recovered quickly, with the exception of Kathleen. In the damp foggy weather she could not summon up the physical reserves to throw off the cold and fever. It went to her lungs and within a week she was dead.

The posts were slow and unpredictable. To reach Aden took anything from four to six weeks. I don't know when Alex heard news of her death. Perhaps it was in the middle of the Aden epidemic, perhaps when it was over and he could feel the blow fully.

Phyllis Sealey says that Kathleen had been a great influence on Alex; they were alike in temperament. Edyth never forgot God's sorrows. Kathleen and Alex worshipped in His joy, seeing in the Crucifixion more the triumph than the physical suffering. While Kathleen lived, Alex was not an exposed person. They sheltered one another. They were like two trees growing close together.

The death of Kathleen left Alex to grow alone. It was the second stage of his singling out, the first being that strange snapping of the engagement to Phyllis.

After the recovery from the influenza epidemic, the *Topaze* was despatched to Bombay to refit. Alex had already taken her there for an earlier refit, in 1917, and he knew how malarial the docks were. Officers like Brook thought he was exhibiting an unnecessary enthusiasm when he pressed on the work of refitting with a relentless energy. The War was over. The fleshpots were attractive. Why couldn't the old man relax?

I am sure that Alex knew that he himself was ill, just as Kathleen had known for nights in the hospital before she collapsed. Fired by her example, he would not give up but drove on so relentlessly because he felt his reserves giving out.

He took the *Topaze* out of Bombay refitted but he did not bring her into Aden. He was taken ashore at Hodeida, suffering from malaria; and soon after that he was invalided home. The fever made him so groggy that no naval doctor inquired whether there was anything else wrong with his legs.

CHAPTER EIGHT

ALEX arrived home on Sunday 11 May 1919. During the voyage his health had improved. The violence of the malaria had abated. But he was very weak and his legs were groggier than they had ever been.

His father took him to Haslar Hospital for a thorough check-up. He was examined by three doctors, all of whom were intent on the possible after-effects of malaria. They found that there was no enlargement of the spleen and that the heart was sound. He had been very ill and what he needed was time to build up his strength.

He reported next day to the Admiralty and was given a month's leave. At the same time he paid a visit to Dr J. B. Mennell, a Harley Street specialist, whom he saw as a private patient. He explained to him what he had concealed from the naval doctors, that his legs had shown a pronounced weakening since the malaria; but he was not certain that the weakness was caused by malaria. It had been there beforehand in a milder degree.

Dr Mennell on examination found a definite atrophy of the peroneal muscle. He was unable to diagnose the cause. But when he heard that Dr Woods was going to Buxton to have treatment for the eczema from which he was suffering acutely, Dr Mennell suggested that Alex should have a course of treatment there also. He advised that Alex should have boots made for him with supports built in to strengthen his legs. They would not cure the disability, but they would conceal it.

The cure at Buxton had no effect. He was still very

weak when he reported to the Admiralty a month later and he was granted six weeks' sick leave without demur. Now that the War was over, all the services were being ruthlessly cut with the Geddes axe and it was pleasant to have one officer who was not begging for a job.

At the end of June Alex was promoted to the rank of captain. But there was no job to be found for him; and so, like hundreds of others, he was placed on half-pay, until suitable employment could be found for him.

He spent his time with the family at Alverstoke. His three brothers were married and had families of their own. While Kathleen had been alive, the Doctor and his wife had been cared for and cherished by her and Edyth, so the others thought. But the death of Kathleen revealed that Edyth was even more helpless than her mother. She had as little *savoir vivre* and she had, into the bargain, been stricken with glaucoma which had robbed her of all but a tiny portion of her vision, sufficient for her to be able to make slow progress about the house and abroad, but insufficient for her to be the help her parents needed. Dr Wood's eyesight was beginning to trouble him and his eczema was almost continuous. His wife, a weaker body, was failing from bronchitis and spent much of her time in bed during the winter months.

Alex, convalescent though he was, appeared in such a household as a pillar of strength. He had saved money from his pay and finding that his father was feeling the pinch, because his pension had remained the same since his retirement while prices had steadily risen, Alex insisted on giving his father some hundreds of pounds. To Alex the chief use of money was to help people who needed it; and his father had no false pride which might refuse the gift.

Just as when he had returned earlier from a long absence aboard, Alex thought of the possibility of marriage. He was thirty-eight. He longed to have a family, as his other brothers had done. And now he could afford to marry.

But as on the previous occasion something happened to intervene; something perfectly explicable by coincidence but which anyone like Howard Marshall would, I realized, have interpreted as the intervention of Divine Providence.

During the War Alex's brother Charles had been invalided home from France with trench feet. He was finding the same difficulty in walking that Alex had found and Alex recommended him to go to Dr Mennell. Perhaps Charles could have some special boots made for him.

Dr Mennell examined Charles Woods briefly, then he became excited and turned up the notes which he had made on Alex's case. The symptoms were identical, a wasting of the peroneal muscle and a certain weakness also in the hands.

"Have any other members of your family had similar symptoms? Your brothers and sisters, for example?"

"My brother Arthur has a certain difficulty with his balance," said the Colonel. "But he lost an arm during the war and that's what it's due to."

"Your father? Your mother?"

"My father is perfectly sound. My mother has a slight weakness. But it's nothing to speak of."

Dr Mennell said there was nothing he could do until he had had a talk with Dr Woods. At his interview with the Doctor he made inquiries about his wife's family, as a result of which Dr Woods went back to Alverstoke and spent some days working on the family tree. This affliction of the legs and hands was traceable back for seven generations. It had never been a total disablement. Among those afflicted were High Court judges, admirals, generals, Members of Parliament and writers. "Which is very interesting," said Dr Mennell. "Hereditary muscular atrophy is normally associated with subnormal ability. But in this case most of those suffering from it are of super-normal ability."

Alex inquired what exactly the word "hereditary" meant and Dr Mennell said it appeared that the children of a parent with the disease stood about a fifty-fifty chance of being healthy, while the children of those who were un-affected would themselves be completely unaffected.*

The knowledge that he suffered from hereditary mus-cular atrophy which might be transmitted to his children determined Alex never to marry. That particular road to happiness was blocked.

It must have been a bitter thing to accept. He was devoted to children and would have loved to play to a son the role that his father had played to him.

Yet Alex had the same conviction that Howard Mar-shall has that God may intervene in the lives of His creatures. Whereas an agnostic might have been filled with self-pity, I suspect that when he had taken in what Dr Mennell had to say, Alex went down on his knees and thanked God that He had not allowed him to marry Phyllis Sealey and bring into the world a family half of whom would have to face the fact that they could only enjoy the fulfilment of marriage at the expense of the next generation.

What a consoling faith this Christianity was! Where any other man would have been filled with sorrow and bitterness at being deprived of healthy children, the Christian could thank God that his girl-friend jilted him and find evidence in that of God's providence! And of course Alex wouldn't have stopped there. If God didn't

* This conclusion was borne out by the further investigation of Dr Hierons, who said of the disease itself, "I have seen so many diseases which are really horrifying that progressive muscular atrophy appears to me quite trifling. In fact I wouldn't particularly mind having it myself. It merely means that if an afflicted person walks five miles he is as fatigued as an unafflicted person would be after twenty miles."

want him to marry and settle down and have children, He must have some other plan for him, some special work for which his disability was a qualification.

I believe that if there was any single moment of vision in which Alex realized that God had called him to live a life different from that of other Christians, it was after Dr Mennell had diagnosed that he was suffering from hereditary muscular atrophy.

I do not want to make even this appear sensational. Alex was a truly humble man. He would have shrunk from the idea that God had picked him out for a special task, because he was conscious of his own inadequacy. (And also, as a natural conformist, he must have shrunk from a call which might take him into uncharted regions of the spirit.)

It is probable that his vocation to Holy Orders came from this time, but not necessarily the precise form which it should take. Nor was it, I think, an immediate call. Alex realized that his first task was to care for his father and mother in their old age. He may have felt that when the time came to give himself completely to God, it must be a devotion unshackled by other duties and loyalties. Or, if God gave the instructions, the call might have been for later on, with the years between a preparation, a long novitiate.

At any rate there was no outward change after he heard Dr Mennell's verdict. He waited on half-pay until April 1920, when he was appointed "to the *President*, additional, for special service inside Admiralty, 26 April; and for duty with *President* N.I.A.C.C., to date 1 May 1920."

The *President* in this enigmatic posting was not a ship or naval establishment, but Vice-Admiral Sir Edward Charlton, President of the Naval Inter-Allied Commission of Control in Germany. The function of N.I.A.C.C. was to ensure that the enemy observed the naval conditions laid down in the various peace treaties. Ships and naval equipment had to be handed over or destroyed. Naval defences had to be dismantled, submarine-pens and gun-emplacements demolished. Factories and yards devoted to naval construction had to be invigilated. Arsenals had to be searched for hidden caches of arms and so on.

It was a stimulating task for those engaged in the field work, made more complicated by the revolutionary conditions of such towns as Hamburg, where naval officers found to their dismay that Communists were offering their dubious assistance in the liquidation of Junkerism.

Over it all presided Vice-Admiral Sir Edward Charlton, who won for himself the odd distinction of being the only admiral in Berlin who went to work and back on a motor-scooter. From his Berlin office there proceeded at quarterly intervals enormous reports on the progress of the Commission of Control, through which ran monotonously the complaint that the German authorities were doing everything in their power to circumvent the terms of the peace treaty. These reports, plus an occasional telegram requesting the diversion of some unit of the Royal Navy from the Baltic to take the President to inspect the progress of the demolitions at Heligoland, would come through to Alex at the Admiralty. His task consisted in supervising the printing of the progress reports and their circulation to the interested departments, besides the day-to-day liaison between the President of N.I.A.C.C. in Berlin and the Admiralty in London.

It was not a difficult task. If it had not involved material of a secret nature, it could have been done equally well by a Grade A clerk. As it was, it provided Alex with a job, which brought him in, with allowances, £1,375 a year, and enabled him every week-end to go down to Alverstoke to see his family.

There are only two clues to his private activity in London. The first is that given by Lettice—his love of walking in St James's Park during the luncheon break and his fear that the peculiar gait he had, even using the special boots, would bring discredit on his uniform, because people might think that he was drunk. The second is a postcard to his father, saying that he had entertained a mutual friend by taking him round his favourite London churches. Church-crawling was a family pastime—the first thing which he and his father had done on arriving at Dartmouth was to look round the parish church. It was the devout man's version of the pub-crawl, a connoisseurship of the different architectural and decorative tributes to the glory of God.

I imagine also that during this London period Alex luxuriated in the opportunity for daily Communion. There had been no chaplain on the *Topaze* and his opportunities for taking Holy Communion had been confined to the periods in port. This had produced a terrible sense of spiritual privation.

When the work of N.I.A.C.C. was completed in 1922, Alex was given command of H.M.S. *Greenwich*, a depot ship for the repair of destroyers at sea. In the words of one of his officers, Lieutenant (now Commander) Ashton, this was "about as low as one could sink". Alex comforted him by pointing out that at least it was a job, and at that time large numbers of naval officers were unemployed.

Ashton was a young officer and in his eyes Alex was "extremely well read, far above the average naval officer"—a view held by no other witness. He had his officers to dinner in his cuddy in turn. Although he was "most abstemious himself, he kept an exceptional table".

The only vivid memory I have [Ashton adds] was one day at General Drill during an Admiral's inspection. My language during the heat of some evolution was not of the best, and when it was all over he went for me on the subject and I had a pretty severe dressing down, but although he left me in no doubt as to what he thought of bad language, it was a very kindly dressing down and I merely felt very humiliated. He never held it up against me and we had many sailing picnics together, a pastime we both enjoyed.

He was intensely religious then and Holy Communion was held every Sunday in his day-cabin, but he was not a "bible thumper".

Admiral of the Fleet Lord Cunningham of Hyndhope was in those days commanding one of the destroyers which used the *Greenwich* as a depot ship. I asked him what he thought of Alex in this command.

A depot ship is a floating workshop [he answered]. The officer in command ought to be an engineer; and of course Sammy did not know the first thing about engineering. It was typical that he press-ganged the carpenters off the first destroyer that came alongside for repairs and put them on to turning his day-cabin into a chapel. He was very proud of an altar-cloth which had been made for him by his sister. He kept it in a chest and produced it on the slightest provocation.

The Chaplain who officiated aboard the *Greenwich* was a Low Church Welshman named Jones. Alex had long arguments with him about the sacramental approach to worship as opposed to the didactic. He converted the Welshman to the Anglo-Catholic view and with a convert's ardour he threw himself into ritualistic practice, as bigotedly its professor as he had been formerly its opponent.

Contingents from the destroyer flotilla came aboard the depot ship each Sunday for Church Parade; and an officer from one of the destroyers, a sincere Low Churchman, was so outraged by these Popish practices at a service which men were forced to attend as a parade that he wrote to the Admiralty. Jones was reprimanded.

I have no evidence, but I think that Alex would have

agreed with the reprimand. He never maintained that the sacramental was the only way to worship God. He went no further than saying that for him, a sinner, it was the most helpful. He would certainly have disapproved of any practice, helpful as it might be to him, if it outraged the conscience of any sincere Christian who had no other choice of Christian service.

While he was in command of the *Greenwich*, he made his most rigorous exercise in asceticism. He resolved to fast during the forty days of Lent. This resolution, I think, did not spring from the negative desire to mortify the flesh. It was an act of love, an offering to God in recognition of Christ's far greater sacrifice, the spontaneous tribute of a saintly man.

But as well as being a saintly man, Alex was Captain of the *Greenwich*, which during Lent was engaged on spring manœuvres. During these the Captain had to be on the bridge day and night. The strain was too great and Alex collapsed from sheer exhaustion in a faint. The Surgeon Commander was summoned and immediately called for brandy. By this time Alex had recovered consciousness. He realized what was happening and protested that he would take no stimulant. "You are the Captain of the ship," said the Surgeon Commander, "and you can give orders to everyone but me. When you are sick, I give orders to you. Now drink that up, sir. That is an order."

Alex grinned feebly. "Aye, aye, sir." And he drank it up.

Once again he had been brought face-to-face with the difficulty of being at the same time a naval officer and a man of God.

One of my correspondents was a naval chaplain who had known Alex when he was King's Harbourmaster and Captain of the Yard. I drove over to Woking to see him, hoping that he might be able to give me more details of

Alex's spiritual life in the Navy than I had got from his fellow-officers.

The information he had to give me about Alex was valuable only in a negative way. He had never discussed the possibility of taking Holy Orders (though I learned subsequently that Alex had mentioned it to Phyllis Sealey, when the *Greenwich* put in at Liverpool. He talked as if it were a decision he had arrived at some time before). He had never talked with the Chaplain about his own spiritual problems. Their discussions of religion were always in general terms.

I said to the Chaplain, "Mustn't Alex have appeared a very strange creature as a naval officer?"

His answer interested me. "In all the years that I was a naval chaplain, I never met a sailor who was an atheist. Atheism is tenable if you live in a city, a man-dominated environment. But at sea you can't not-believe in God. You can be lax, you can take Him for granted, you can use Him only when you want Him. But the sea is God-dominated. You can't pretend He's not there."

He told me of a ship off which a rating was rushed to hospital, very ill. The Captain told the crew about it at Divisions. "The doctor says he will probably die," he said, "but let us pray God that he will live." The prayer was made in a matter-of-fact way, a simple request for a favour from God.

At Divisions the next day the Captain said. "Almighty God answered our prayers yesterday. Our man rallied almost immediately, for no reason the doctors can understand. He is now out of danger. Let us thank Him for this miracle."

I asked the Chaplain whether as a result of this real or apparent answer to prayer there was any sort of religious revival among the ship's crew. It seemed to me, if true, the most wonderful thing.

The Chaplain shook his head. "That's what I am trying

to tell you," he said. "It made no noticeable difference. Why should it? They believed in miracles anyway. If they hadn't, the man wouldn't have recovered."

To a sailor with a simple unfanatic belief in God, I realized Alex must have appeared strange in quite a different way from that in which he appeared strange to me. As an agnostic I could not possibly understand how he could hold the beliefs he did; but if those beliefs were true, then a devotion as total, a dedication as complete as Alex's was the only possible attitude, as far as I could see. For the truth of Christianity, if it were true, transcended all other truths. And how sad it was that it was not true!

But to the naturally believing seaman, who took for granted that a God existed who so loved His creature, man, that he had given His only Son that all who believed in Him might be saved, Alex might have appeared as someone who was making too great a fuss about something which everyone sensible knew to be true. This concern about God might appear as strange, as if somebody couldn't get over the fact that there was oxygen in the air we breathe.

I understood what was the basis of Alex's lifelong championship of seamen. He ranted against the popular prejudice against sailors ashore, their drunkenness, their womanizing and their shiftlessness; because he saw that they had a far deeper faith in Jesus Christ than many of the respectable citizens who condemned them. Their faults, the very existence of which he sometimes denied in the ardour of his advocacy, were due to the stresses of their trade; the unnatural confinement aboard ship without opportunities for relaxation and enjoyment, the brief periods in foreign ports where the pretence of friendship and love was offered for sale, and even at home the emotional difficulties of taking up family life where it was left off months before. I suspect that Alex's championship of sailors was not purely that of a very good man for lesser men whose goodness he could perceive. I think that it was the defence of men from whom he himself had learnt things about the nature of good and evil and the relation of man to God which he might not otherwise have discovered.

I was puzzled and surprised by the absence of priggishness in Alex. He had no wild oats period as St Augustine had. There was no spiritual rebellion, no outbreak of sexual licence, no drunkenness, no wavering of faith. Yet he was never goody-goody or self-righteous. He had an instinctive understanding of the things which came between his fellow-men and God, which was not derived from personal experience.

One can of course say with truth that he derived this from the study of the life and teachings of Jesus Christ. No one was sharper in his distinction between the appearance and reality of good and evil. The Gospels provided him with the theory of Christianity; the Royal Navy gave him its practice. How frequently he must have discovered the source of goodness beneath the crust of vice and dissipation among the men with whom he served, and what strength he must have derived from their deep-seated though unvoiced belief in God! The vices which were destructive of the soul were not drunkenness (the search for the Infinite through alcohol) or lust (a debased form of the Love which is God). They were selfishness, envy, greed, pride and self-righteousness. Like Jesus Christ, he was harder on those who in observing the letter of religion have lost the spirit, the Pharisees, the self-preeningly religious, the little Jack Horners of conventional Christianity.

If I am right in thinking this, the period which he spent in the Royal Navy after he had resolved that he would ultimately take Holy Orders was not a waste of time, but a preparation, during which he learned many things which were to prove useful.

As far as I can discover, he never again attempted a rigorous fast during Lent. When I asked his friend Dr Bullitt, with whom Alex lunched every Sunday when he was at the Sailors' Home, Bullitt said it was possible that during Lent he might have eaten rather less than usual, but it was not so much less that he had ever noticed. He added, "He had really no need for the practice of asceticism. The atrophy in his legs and hands imposed a discipline on him, sharper than most people impose on themselves during Lent."

I think it is possible that Alex took the failure of his fast on the *Greenwich* as a lesson in moderation. As Dr Bullitt pointed out, his progressive muscular atrophy was a form of asceticism physically imposed, and Alex was making quite a sufficient offering to God by behaving as if the disability did not exist and ignoring the fatigue in his legs. He may have reached the conclusion that God did not want from him further sacrifices of privation. God demanded from no one more than he could give.

He may have found another example of this in the matter of daily Communion. Having a chaplain at last, Alex wanted to use him to the full. He himself had developed a positive hunger for daily Communion and he thought how wonderful it would be if every man aboard the *Greenwich* were given the chance. "I don't want to force them," he said to the officer responsible. "Let them have half an hour free from any duties. If they want to take Communion, they can." He smiled at the officer. "Just rearrange the board, will you?"

The officer went away and examined the routine board. Short of getting the whole ship up half an hour earlier, there was no way of finding the time. So the officer returned to the Captain with the routine board and said, "I wonder if you'd mind, sir, just indicating what we should drop in cleaning ship and equipment to make room for this half-hour?"

"I remember the pained and hurt look on Woods's face," the officer wrote to me, "when after long consideration he told me that he could not see where that half-hour could be made available without adversely affecting the cleanliness and efficiency of the ship. A compromise was arranged whereby any man might get permission to attend the service, provided that he could be spared from duty."

Alex's command of the *Greenwich* was on the whole pretty happy. (If there had been a war, with the more violent strains it produces, this might not have been so.) The most damning criticism of the command was that, as a destroyer repair ship, the *Greenwich* did not repair destroyers very well. Alex was not a "nuts and bolts man"; but the Navy was steadily becoming a nuts and bolts Navy. An officer who lacked advanced technical training was soon to be regarded as a liability.

Alex did not remain in the Navy long enough to become conscious of the need either to get out or to go back to school and learn a lot of new skills. He had only one further command afloat and the importance of that was more diplomatic than naval.

As a result of the First World War, the Dominions had evolved small navies of their own, which in peacetime were liable to grow stale through operating in their own waters in small formations. To give the Australians experience of working with larger units, it was arranged that one of their cruisers should be exchanged for work with the Home and Mediterranean fleets in return for a British cruiser working in Australian waters.

The importance of the exchange was not merely to obtain familiarity with each other's methods of working. During the War German agents had been at work to stir up bad feeling between the Dominions and the home country and they had not been entirely unsuccessful. Australians and British did not automatically take to one another. Like other people they needed to *make* friends.

The appointment of Captain Woods, D.S.O. and bar, was made after it was decided that H.M.S. *Concord* should return the visit paid by H.M.S. *Adelaide* to home waters. The choice was shrewd. Whoever picked Alex had seen what a success Jellicoe had proved as Governor-General of New Zealand; the little, quiet, God-loving Admiral whose authority issued from within. Australians expecting some bluff sea dog, with the whites of his blue eyes pink with gin and angostura bitters, would get a shock at this handsome creature who, the moment he stepped ashore, made a bee-line for the nearest church.

It was intended that the *Concord* should spend six months in Australian waters, but the visit was curtailed at each end. The *Adelaide* was late away and delayed the departure from Malta. Soon after they reached Australia, trouble flaring in the China Sea led to an urgent summons to Hong Kong. The exercises with the Australian Navy went unperformed. There was time only for the junketings, the visits to Sydney, Melbourne, Adelaide and the rest, the sports, the cricket matches, the regattas, the public receptions with the mayors and the private parties with the bishops, the coach tours to the interior and the visits of schoolgirls over the cruiser.

Mishaps were few. The first night they left a man ashore among reputed cannibals, but by the next morning he had not been eaten. Conscious of their semi-ambassadorial mission, the ratings seduced no girls, while preserving attitudes of gallantry wherever they went. Considering the temptations placed before them, few got badly drunk. Alex's scrapbook of the trip reads like a protracted Sunday school outing.

His officers were frightened that a captain so modest would fail in his public appearances; but his voice, without much body in private conversation, carried wonderfully in the open and in large halls and his public per-

135

sonality charmed the Australians. There was, one news-paper announced, only one further service which the Captain of the *Concord* might do and that was to marry an Australian, as a good example to his men.

There could have been no better choice than Alex as a sailor-diplomat. But he was not destined to command her in far-eastern waters. On arrival at Hong Kong, he handed her over and transferred to the *Diomed* with instructions to bring her home.

This was his last voyage. On his return he was given a Senior Officers' Technical Course at Portsmouth in October 1925, and the next year he was appointed to Portsmouth Dockyards, as Captain of the Yard, Deputy Superintendent and King's Harbourmaster.

To what extent his wishes were consulted I do not know. He would certainly not have ordered things differently if he had been given the choice. His mother had died in March 1921, unobtrusively as she had lived. "My dearest Lillie sinks," the Doctor wrote on her last day, "but knowing us all until shortly before death—embracing us—kissing us—pointing to one and all, smiling constantly as if perfectly happy—at 8 p.m. a few short breaths and gone to Paradise. I thank the Father Almighty for vouchsafing such a wonderful end—taking her from this world of sin and sorrow."

Her death had not been a great surprise. She had been a semi-invalid for some years, lacking her mother's tenacious grip on life.

Edyth's eyes retained a glimmer of vision. The glaucoma had not completely blinded her. Though she was unable to read, she had a small undamaged area of vision which enabled her to move without assistance. The Doctor's left eye had also suffered a glaucosis, and the year after his wife's death a cataract began to form in the right eye.

In those days the operation for the removal of a cataract was still a recent thing; no form of anæsthesia had been evolved for it. Dr Woods was warned of this and told that the operation would be painful. He did not mind this. He was able to bear pain.

He said afterwards that he had not been told that there would be a sudden very sharp pain as they cut in with the knife. If he had been warned, he could have borne it without flinching. As it was, his head gave an involuntary jerk and the knife plunged into the eye. There was nothing to do but remove it altogether.

So there they were in the big house at Alverstoke, Edyth and her father, the purblind looking after the blind.

Dorothy Woods kept an eye on them, but she had her husband and children to attend to. Alex felt himself to be the person who should look after his father, and the appointments in Portsmouth enabled him to do so without interfering with his naval career.

In November 1928 the appointment at the Dockyard ended. He was offered the command of another ship, but he refused it. There are different stories why, all based on what he said at one time or another. There were two other officers married and with children, either of whom needed the job more than he. He did not see himself climbing aboard up a rope ladder. If it had been that he felt his father had grown so infirm that he could not be left with Edyth, he would not have said so openly. But I think that was probably the most powerful of his motives; that and the realization that when his father died he would retire from the Royal Navy.

From November 1928 to 3 April 1931, Alex remained on the Active List but without a job, living at Alverstoke on half-pay. During that time he saw his father through his last illness.

On 3 April 1931 he was promoted to Rear-Admiral and the next day he was placed on the retired list.

I asked one of his nieces whether she remembered what

her uncle was like at this time. She answered that she remembered him very well. They had all gone bathing at Stokes Bay and Uncle Alex unlike most people had entered the water in a straw boater. He had walked out further and further until the sea came first over his shoulders and then over his head. At this point the straw boater became waterborne and she and the other children watched it miserably because from the way it was bobbing about it was plain that Uncle Alex was drowned. None of them wanted to make too much of a fuss about it though. They were glad because Uncle appeared in the sea some way off and not even the hat was drowned.

This glimpse of Uncle Alex is needed as an antidote to what might otherwise be too solemn a view of a devoted son, a tender-hearted sea captain and a daily communicant.

CHAPTER NINE

Alex approached the Bishop of London, who approved of his taking Holy Orders. In view of his age and knowledge, a two-years' course should be sufficient; and he recommended that Alex should go to Cheshunt for his training.

The staff of Bishop's College, Cheshunt, found the prospect alarming. There was no rule against a rear-admiral entering a theological college as a student, though it had never happened before and was unlikely to happen again. It was not merely his rank. It was also his age. He was fifty-two, four years older than the Reverend R. H. Moberly, the Principal; and the Vice-Principal, George Inglis, who would be responsible for the supervision of the Admiral's studies, was twenty years younger than his naval pupil.

But they had only to meet Alex to discover that there was never a man less like the caricatures of admirals popularized by the cartoonist, H. M. Bateman, at that time. "You're in command," was his opening phrase; "just tell me what to do."

There was another elderly student, a Lieutenant-Colonel from the Indian Army, also by chance called Inglis. Alex and Lieutenant-Colonel Inglis struck up a friendship. They were known to the others as the Old Gang. As such they won an immensely popular victory in the three-legged race at the annual sports. As such they exercised an influence over the younger students for the acceptance of the college discipline. If they, so accus-

tomed to command, were so obedient, there was no justi-
fication for junior revolt. "It was the very opposite of
what we expected," both Moberly and Inglis said. "The
older men weren't set in their ways. They took everything in their stride. In fact, with the Admiral it was
sometimes difficult to make him see that he couldn't be
treated like an ordinand of twenty-three."

The Vice-Principal gave him essays to write, instead of
the usual set books and papers. "The matter was excellent," he said. "He knew his Bible thoroughly. He could
not write a sentence apparently. And then I realized
that what he was doing was to make a series of heads,
perhaps rather like the signals which he had sent as a
Signals Officer. He said to me, 'I really haven't written
anything for over thirty years. But I'll do my best.' He
tried, but he never had a flow. He was not that sort of
man."

I knew exactly what the Vice-Principal meant. Among
the papers which Stride had given me were notes for
sermons, written exactly as his original Cheshunt notes
must have been written. I looked them through, but they
meant nothing to me.

It was terrifying. I had gradually penetrated the
family secrets; and they amounted to very little. He
loved his father and mother, his brothers and sisters, a girl
called Phyllis Sealey who jilted him. But his love for them
was only a reflection, as it seemed, of his love for God. I
had thought that in the progressive muscular atrophy I
should find some spectacular disability or agonizing pain.
But that was nothing more than a barrier to marriage, a
fingerpost to Cheshunt. These were not the subjects of
the book; they were the extranea. What made him fast
during the spring manœuvres? That hunger for the
sacrament of Holy Communion? They were the symptoms of whatever existed between Alex and God. I knew
beyond any doubt that there was something there of im-

mense importance to Alex for it to have taken him down to the Red Ensign Club and have kept him in the East End for twenty years. But what was it? I had felt when Lettice Woods and Howard Marshall had been talking of the Divine Will operating in and around this book as if they lived in a Cloudcuckooland. But it appeared to me now to be a continent less crazy if Alex had been able to live there so long and so sanely.

"What did *you* make of Alex Woods?" I asked Moberly.*

"He reminded me in many ways of Winnington Ingram, before he became Bishop of London. He had the same simplicity of faith, the same natural goodness, the same potentiality of sainthood."

I had never considered the variety offered within the Church to its ministers or reflected that for a clergyman to reach his full stature he needs the suitable place and occasion as much as a politician, a soldier and even an artist does. I would not foist this upon Canon Moberly, but as a result of what he said, it occurred to me that Winnington Ingram might have reached a greater spiritual stature as a parish priest than he did as Bishop of London. His touch was personal; he had a genuine gift of intimacy which could have thrived in parochial work. Spread over too many people, as it inevitably was in the episcopal field, it took on a quality of insincerity. He had to pretend to the intimacies he could have achieved in a smaller field; or else he could have admitted to himself that a bishop could not, and should not be expected to, achieve this personal contact. It was his vanity that led him to attempt to treat his diocese as a parish.

For Alex, the Bishop of London conceived a warm

* I call him Moberly, though I thought of him as "the Dean". When I saw him he was Canon Moberly, Dean of Salisbury. Before then, and while Alex was at the Red Ensign Club, he was Bishop of Stepney. And earlier still, the Principal of Cheshunt. A most elusive personality, of which the name Moberly was the only constant.

enough feeling to claim him as "a lifelong friend". And yet it is interesting that in the two letters which Alex preserved from the Bishop almost identical phrases occur. "I often think of you in the *Iron Duke* and the flag you gave me," reads the first. "How well I remember meeting you in the *Iron Duke*, and the flag you gave me," runs the second.

One can see the mental process. The Bishop gets a letter from a chap called Woods, a naval officer. Who on earth is he? He searches through the naval files of his memory. Of course, the signals officer who gave him the Jellicoe deployment flag. Down goes the recognition sentence, that "intimate touch" which is the very opposite of intimacy; which merely says, "Isn't it wonderful that a busy bishop like me can remember which Woods you are of all the Woodses that I have had to meet in the course of my work?"

In a sense it was wonderful, but not as an activity of the spirit; merely as a feat of memory. It was gratifying to be thus remembered—and when the Bishop in effecting an introduction added, "my lifelong friend", emotion was added to gratitude. "Here indeed," people felt, "is a man with a great capacity for love. I have only seen him briefly half a dozen times in my life and yet he looks on me as a lifelong friend."

It was different when the Bishop introduced his "lifelong friends" Smith and Jones to one another as Brown and Robinson. This happened with increasing frequency as the parts of his brain devoted to the memory of names and faces became congested.

Alex himself would never have made such a criticism of the Bishop aloud. He had evolved or come to accept a discipline of the tongue, framed in seven questions.

1. Is this of which I was going to speak to his discredit?
2. Will it lower him if known?
3. Is it to my certain knowledge true?

4. If I had done it myself, should I like it spoken of?
5. Is it important for the sake of warning that it should be known to the person to whom I was going to speak?
6. Am I the proper person to mention it?
7. Am I prepared to stand by my words, or do I intend to end up with, "Don't mention me, I beg"?

This questionnaire, pasted in the second of his cipher log scrapbooks, puzzled me. It is a carbon copy and its significance depends on who composed and typed it. Was it Alex himself?

In that case he would have designed it for the instruction of other people and was keeping this carbon for reference.

To me this is inconceivable. Even though he obviously approved of its intention as a guide to his own discretion, I cannot imagine his ever presuming to instruct others on such a subject, or at any rate in such language. He wrote, as he spoke, a natural colloquial English, not in any way impressive, nor by the same token as depressing as "Don't mention me, I beg". If my estimate of his character is right, he could not have written the questionnaire in the first place, have typed it in the second, or finally have pasted it in his scrapbook as testimony to his achievement in the literature of edification.

He must have been given it; and this implies conversation with someone about the sins of evil and careless speech, a subject which certain religious types are prepared to discuss with all and sundry. But not Alex. The testimony of everyone is that he was a very religious man, with High Church views; but not that he talked about religion or Christian conduct. He impressed by his significant reticence.

I thought for a time that Alex must have been given the questionnaire by his confessor and that this would give me the clue as to when he started confession. But I was wrong. One of his fellow-ordinands at Cheshunt, an ex-policeman called Jones, tells me that he made his first confession on his instigation. He had a strong psychological resistance against confession, based on the usual evangelical argument that in self-examination he needed no assistance except what he could obtain from God and his conscience. Jones persuaded him to try confession as a spiritual aid, and thenceforward he maintained the practice for the rest of his life. He followed the Anglican practice of making two or three detailed confessions a year, a periodic stocktaking; and not the Roman Catholic practice of the necessarily perfunctory confession before every communion.

It is clear from this that someone, probably a clergyman to whom he had talked of his difficulties as a commanding officer, had given him the questionnaire when he was aboard H.M.S. *Concord*.

I found such serious examination of the tongue a rather unsympathetic discipline. Like most writers, I recognize the value of gossip. A great many short stories and novels are scandal raised by imagination to the level of art; it seems to me a legitimate exercise to speculate about the secret thoughts and motives of one's neighbour. I am not concerned with Madame X and Mr Y themselves; they are the ports of imaginative departure for voyages on which it is possible to discover strange new countries of the mind. All writers when they gather together indulge in forms of slanderous speculation about one another in ways which disgust their non-professional friends. Their conversation would not pass any of the seven hurdles of Alex's questionnaire. But I would passionately defend it as a harmless literary pastime, productive of healthy laughter and sometimes even of creative ideas.

Alex's discipline was not designed for a writer, but for himself as the captain of a ship, inevitably privy to many secrets of his officers and men which should be divulged only in very special circumstances. Like a priest, a doctor or a lawyer, a ship's captain has to exercise a more than ordinary discretion. He must be trusted and no one will be prepared to trust a man who is liable to pass on information merely in order to make friends and influence people.

As naval officer or priest, Alex appeared to me as a dull man. The reputation for dullness is a penalty paid for being discreet. But what lay beneath the dullness, below that gentleness; not in the mind—that was ordinary enough—but in the spirit?

"He was very wise in the spirit," said Canon Moberly. "And also humorous. He made jokes about God. Always in the most reverent way, you must understand; but he could joke about Him."

"Was he sentimental?" I asked, thinking of *Winnie the Pooh* and the religious postcards.

"Intensely. He used to take me to the Naval Tournament at Olympia and sit there with tears streaming down his cheeks. He would go three or four times each year, with different parties, and it didn't make any difference how often he went. He always wept."

Sentimentality has now an implication of mawkishness and the desire to cultivate the easier emotions of tenderness because of the belief that a lump in the back of the throat is evidence of the highest sensibility. Alex was not sentimental in this way. He responded simply to appeals to the emotions. He loved Charlie Chaplin as a film artist—and as with everyone he loved, he placed him beyond criticism. Eucharis Woods was appalled at certain vulgarities in the early Chaplins. There was one in which Charlie rode through a church on a donkey. Eucharis thought it was blasphemous. Alex roared with laughter. "But if it had been Buster Keaton or Harold Lloyd, Alex would have been terribly shocked."

Alex could not resist an appeal to genuine emotions; even if it was not a genuine appeal. But he was sharp

EC–K

enough to detect appeals to false emotions, even if their manner was fresh.

During the 'twenties his favourite inspirational reading was provided by the Reverend Studdert Kennedy, popularly known as "Woodbine Willie", a great translator of Christian teaching into the idiom of the troops, a preacher with a punch. Alex would await the new Woodbine Willie with tense excitement and present copies of it to any young rating he felt might benefit.

After Cheshunt, his favourite inspirational reading, at any rate for his faithful parishioners, consisted in short studies of Bishop Lancelot Andrewes, of whom it is possible that he had learnt little or nothing before he went to the Theological College. Alex's choice of Anglo-Catholicism had been intuitive and emotional. As an Anglo-Catholic priest, he would be called on to justify that choice, especially by Low Churchmen who could see it as nothing but a betrayal of the English Reformation to the Church of Rome. And in the person and teachings of the sixteenth-century Andrewes, Alex found the clearest exponent and exemplar of English Catholicism.

Lancelot Andrewes was a person so many-sided, a great scholar, a great churchman and a saint, that he draws to himself people of diverse temperaments, who have little in common with one another except what they have in common with him.

Alex used to explode with rage when anyone described himself as a "Protestant". The Christian religion was to Alex the worship of God the Father, God the Son and God the Holy Ghost as revealed through Jesus Christ; and that must be the basis of any Christian church. The "Protestant" had turned away from the worship of God to a permanent protest against the Roman Catholic worship of God.

146

Alex found in Andrewes the Churchman the proposition of a positive religion, stripped of the "idolatries" of
Rome and free from the protestations of nonconformity;
an English Catholic religion directly succeeding from the
Church Christ Jesus founded upon Peter. For the
scholarship of Andrewes, the ability to back any thought
of his own with authority from Latin, Greek or Hebrew,
Alex had little use. ("I've a brain like Winnie the Pooh.")
But the great power of Andrewes's mind was that he
never lost sight of the fundamental principles of the
Christian dogma, and that at a time when men of equal
cleverness were dissipating their energies in sterile controversy.

> Blessed be God [wrote Andrewes in the *Responsio ad
> Apologiam Cardinalis Bellarmini*]. Blessed be God that among
> divers other mysteries about which there are so many mists
> and clouds of controversies raised in all ages and even in
> this of ours, hath left us some clear and without controversy;
> manifest and yet great; and again great and yet manifest.
> So great as no exception to be taken; so manifest as no ques-
> tion to be made about them. Withal, to reform our judge-
> ments in this point. For a false conceit is crept into the minds
> of men, to think the points of religion that be manifest to be
> certain petty points scarce worth the hearing. Those yea
> those be great and none but those, that have great disputes
> about them. It is not so. . . . These that are necessary He
> hath made plain; those that are not plain, not necessary.

Lancelot Andrewes was himself one of the great
preachers of his time. His sermons lacked the rotund
elegance of his young protégé, John Donne, the fancies
which made Donne's *Devotions* and *Death's Duell* rich to
read. Andrewes's sermons were for the pulpit, made to
be spoken, the rhythms broken like conversation. They
are not easy to read, until you get what must have been
the emphases; but these, once got, bring to you how
Andrewes spoke. One can hear the tones of his voice and
follow the darting of his mind.

Since he was master of the sermon, Andrewes might have been pardoned if he had held preaching high. But he warned against it, over and over again. Too great an emphasis, he said, was laid upon the sermon; but not enough on the sacramental elements of the service.

That again was something which Alex applauded. Alex took great pains with his sermons and was capable of adapting them to suit the congregation. He preached just as well as he possibly could. But he saw the danger that the sermon might come between the congregation and God, the more likely so if it was eloquent. To Alex the sacramental element was all but completely important.*

In view of Alex's inability, or refusal, to frame his religious beliefs, I felt that I might succeed in discovering what they were by a general study of Lancelot Andrewes. From the library of my vicar, while he was away on holiday, I pilfered *The Preces Privatae of Lancelot Andrewes, Bishop of Winchester*, introduced and edited by Canon F. E. Brightman, Methuen 1903. And in the introduction I found this statement of the Bishop's views.

> In broad outline the theology which he preached, and in which he apparently hoped that the practice of that which is out of controversy would generally issue, is the Creed, professed by a Catholic Church, wherein the Holy Ghost, through a ministry of apostolic succession and divine right, regenerates men in baptism, confirms them by the imposition of hands, in the exercise of the keys, "the Church's act", by which "God ordinarily proceedeth", feeds them with the body and blood of Christ our Lord in the most holy mysteries of the Eucharist, which impart what they represent, in which there is at once a sacrifice and a communion. In the Church, men, "not trusting in their own righteousness", are to live in faith and hope and love, in a disciplined life of penitence and its fruits and obedience to the command-

* The People's Churchwarden of St Paul's, Dock Street, a very Low Churchman, was appalled by Alex's proposing, as a joke, that the pulpit should be removed from the church.

ments, in prayer and fasting and almsgiving, bringing forth the fruit of the Spirit in order, peace and comeliness.

I copied this passage out, hoping that doing so would make its meaning plain to me.

Canon Brightman had chosen his words carefully. I could tell this from the way it was written. It must mean *something*. But on what level of experience? If it was the Canon's, I might believe that it was a purely incantatory level. But I couldn't see Alex believing in something on a purely incantatory level. He might try and fast during spring manœuvres, but on the whole he was a very practical man. Would he have made head or tail of the broad outline of the theology of Lancelot Andrewes? Or would he have said, "I've got the brains of Winnie the Pooh," and left these obscurities to others?

I seemed to be getting nowhere through the study of Lancelot Andrewes and I turned back to what it was which everyone seemed to agree the Padre possessed. To Badham, the Welfare Officer at the Red Ensign Club, it was "a personality which made you feel at your best", to others he was "gentle", "modest", "deeply religious", "a saint". Some found he had a wonderful sense of humour, but nobody could remember any very funny joke. All these qualities appeared to me facets of something within, a sort of "luminous secret" which came from the depth of his very spirit.

That luminous secret had been with him right from the beginning of his life. It had grown steadily brighter, despite the frustrations or fortified by them. There was no sign of any conversion, no change in his nature. It grew steadily more itself, or God's; it was something describable in either way with equal truth.

When he was at Cheshunt, he was offered a curacy at the fashionable St George's, Hanover Square, one of the smart West End churches. He refused it and I could understand many reasons why. He had come to dislike the rich and complacent, cushioned from God by material comfort. To be exhibited before them, the Rear-Admiral in orders, to be asked to cocktail parties, to be pitied because of his legs and laughed at because he hadn't read T. S. Eliot . . . No, the curacy of St George's, Hanover Square, was no more Alex's parish than the Bishopric of London had been Winnington Ingram's way to holiness.

Alex wanted to be with people who were so poor that they turned to God naturally because they had no one else to turn to; where people were not so physically perfect that they'd take any notice of an old clergyman shambling along in irons; where there were lots of sailors with their special forms of loneliness and their ultimate belief in God; where there was no need to practise self-imposed austerities, because every day imposed its own austerities; where people fasted not out of love for Jesus, but because they were broke, because there was enough food only for the children, because the money for more had been poured down their gullets.

Alex chose the Red Ensign Club, I was going to write, because it gave him all that he needed for spiritual perfection. I think it did, but I am sure that the reason why he chose the job was because he thought that God had told him to go there. That was the "no earthly command," of which he spoke to Lettice.

But before exploring what happened at the Sailors' Home let us examine the origin of the strange story from which this phrase was taken in a distorted form and see what lay behind the lie which caused this book to be written.

PART THREE

CHAPTER TEN

I FIND this a very difficult book to write, because it is necessary to do two things at the same time. I have to present the facts of Alex's life in more or less chronological order, because the experiences which led him to take Holy Orders and devote the last twenty years of his life to work in the East End must be comprehended if the decision is to be understood. Yet this is not a formal biography for reasons which began to be apparent in the first part of the book and will become plainer in this part. It is a search after the truth about Alex Woods, which began with the report of a miracle at Jutland and was continued by me, because I was interested, as an agnostic, in the nature of Christian holiness.

In Part Two I have set out the events of Alex's childhood and service career, as though these were the first things which I discovered. I have had to do this for the sake of clarity. But it is not true to the chronology of my research.

I was pursuing a number of different lines of research at the same time. In one week-end, for example, I visited Lieutenant P. G. Wodehouse, who was one of Alex's earliest shipmates, G. V. Northcote, who was with him on the *Iron Duke*, Lord Cunningham of Hyndhope, who knew him when he commanded the *Greenwich*, and Canon Moberly, who was his Principal at Cheshunt and for some time his Bishop at Stepney. In the week following, I went up to London and in one day saw Dr Hierons, who had investigated the muscular atrophy in the family with

Alex's assistance, Father Groser at St Katharine's Foundation, Butcher Row; Dr Bullitt, Stride and his colleagues at the Sailors' Home and Father Williamson at St Paul's Vicarage, Dock Street.

I had not seen Father Williamson since that initial interview described in Part One. He improved upon acquaintance. He was hasty in his speech, using words impressionistically, capable of what to a person, like myself, used to giving and examining evidence, were gross exaggerations. He talked about the nineteen-twenties, for example, as a time when you could buy beer at a penny a pint (which was true before 1914) whereas after the First World War it was fivepence a pint. It put me on my guard. I could not rely on Father Williamson for matters of fact, unless I had checked and counter-checked them. It wasn't that he was dishonest; it was that the telling phrase came first to his mind and only later did he speculate on its accuracy. It was in fact a compliment that he should talk this way to me, an expression of trust. As I was to find later, he could talk with great precision when he was on his guard.

He was full of ideas during this second visit of mine, and he finished by conducting an elaborate search for various documents which he had accumulated for me. He had some difficulty in finding them, partly because he kept his papers in a disorder nearly as great as I do myself, but also because he was continually distracted by his wife, his curate and the telephone, all bringing him questions demanding immediate attention.

The most important documents which he gave me were a transcript of the original article about the "interposed message" at Jutland and a number of letters which he had received from its author.

This is the text of the article as it appeared, apart from the substitution of a pseudonym for the journalist's name.

ADMIRAL PARSON PREACHES
HIS FIRST SERMON TO SEVEN PEOPLE

BY

Bee Kay

A Rear-Admiral, who entered the Church because of a supernatural revelation received at the Battle of Jutland, preached his first sermon to a congregation of seven people in London's Dockland slums during Christmas.

He is the Reverend Rial Wadham Woods, D.S.O. His theme addressed to the empty pews and white pillars of a church that rises like a gilded lily in one of the meanest streets of Whitechapel, was "Two thousand years ago the inn at Bethlehem was full. Today Christ's house is empty. We have no room for Him."

The reprimand fell from the thin lips and ascetic face of the preacher in the cold, even tones of a quarter-deck sentence.

WHITE-HOT ZEAL

The power of his control was almost frightening when one remembered the white-hot zeal which had driven him to become a deacon at the age of fifty-four.

Seventeen years ago, while he was signalling to the Fleet at the Battle of Jutland, he received an interposed signal which, his sister told me, "came from no Earthly Captain, but from a Higher Command."

Ever since then the admiral has been "under orders". Two years ago he retired from the Navy and entered the theological college; ten days ago he was ordained by the Bishop of London and immediately took up his work as chaplain to the Seamen's Home in Whitechapel.

Now he spends his days among the unemployed hands and other human flotsam and jetsam of the tramp ships; sleeps in a cubicle between stokers, cabin boys, ship's cooks and the remainder of the fo'c'sle, none of whom are more than half English—all because of his "signal".

He will not speak of his experience, nor of his work, except to repeat, very shyly, that he is "under orders".

His parish is perhaps the poorest in London. The service was conducted with the full ritual of the High Church Choral Eucharist. The choir was three times as large as the congregation.

The vicar, who officiated in a mauve and silver cloak between two acolytes, has laboured for years to bring the people in.

This "gilded lily" type of writing is false even when the facts on which it is based are true. The difficulty resides in discovering where embellished truth becomes utter falsehood. It is often impossible to disentangle the truth, because a writer practising this type of journalism is liable to lose the capacity of distinguishing between facts and the catch-news story that can be fabricated from them. The lie on the typewriter becomes the lie in the soul.

I should scarcely have wasted the time in writing to Bee Kay to ask how true her story was. But Father Williamson, with a greater faith in human nature, had discovered her address and written to her.

He was richly rewarded. Bee Kay replied that it was one of the earliest stories she had written. She remembered it very well and she was very glad of the opportunity of telling the truth about it, because her conscience was still uneasy.

This is the story as she told it to Father Williamson and in greater detail in a series of letters to me.

In those days Bee Kay was living, a curious victim of the depression, in a luxury flat in Park Street, Mayfair. Her husband was a famous actor, who was compulsorily "resting" in the United States. His theatrical tour had come to grief and he had sent his family home with the company, while he remained desperately hoping that he might get a job in Hollywood or on Broadway. He could afford to pay his wife no money. She had to fend for herself and her two children, as well as finding £600 a year in rent.

She was apparently unable to sub-let the flat because of its high rent, so she set out to make a living as a free-lance journalist. She scored her initial success with an article on the Depression in New York. It was bought by a popular sensational London newspaper and given a middle-page spread. The economic facts of the depression were gloomy news. But Bee Kay had hit on a way of personalizing misery. The newspaper wanted more of the same stuff.

Bee Kay's mother had a very remarkable charwoman, called Ann Cumming. She had graduated at Edinburgh University and after teaching in a school for some time she had thrown up this career in favour of sharing her lot with the dispossessed. She earned a little money by "charring", which in those days was underpaid and one of the humblest occupations. She slept at Church Army Hostels or Rowton Houses. She ate only the coarsest foods and shared all that she had with those in greater need than herself.

One of the greatest influences in Ann Cumming's life was a woman named Mary Hughes, of whom Father John Groser had spoken to me. Mary Hughes was born in the same street in Mayfair as that in which Bee Kay had her luxury flat. She was the daughter of Judge Hughes, the author of *Tom Brown's Schooldays*, a Christian Socialist and an associate of Frederick Denison Maurice and Charles Kingsley.

Mary Hughes had gone down to the East End originally to live at St Jude's Rectory, Whitechapel, with her sister Lily and her brother-in-law the Reverend Ernest Carter. She worked in the parish of St Jude's and at Toynbee Hall as a social worker; and though the suffering and the helplessness of the lost, the homeless and the ignorant filled her with compassion, she did not stand out from the company of the privileged who had chosen to serve the underprivileged in the East End. It needed something further to reveal to her the peculiar vocation reserved by God, just as for Alex it had needed the jilting of Phyllis Sealey and the discovery of the muscular atrophy. For

Mary Hughes it was the loss of her sister and her brother-in-law in the *Titanic*.

Mary Hughes refused to be consoled. There was no cause for sorrow, she said. It was wonderful they had passed on together.

Everybody agreed that she was never the same after the tragedy. Some people thought that it had affected her reason, sent her off her head. Others, such as her biographer Rosa Hobhouse and Mary's disciple Ann Cumming, believed that this loss cut the strand tying her to conventional Christianity and good works and launched her on a journey of wildly original holiness.

At the time when Bee Kay met Ann Cumming, Mary Hughes had acquired the Dewdrop Inn, in Vallance Road which runs out of the Whitechapel Road nearly opposite the London Hospital. As The Earl Grey, this property had become so notorious that its licence had been taken away. The house had been closed for some time before Mary Hughes was seized with the idea of taking it over and running it as a training centre for social workers. She felt that however Toynbee Hall might have started it had ceased to fulfil its function. People came down to Toynbee Hall and "observed conditions", as though the East Enders were a foreign form of life. The only way to see what life was like in the East End was to live it as the poorest East Ender had to.

It was the same instinct that led Alex living in the Sailors' Home to install no luxuries for himself, but to live as the others did.

Mary Hughes took in all and sundry, the righteous and the unrighteous, the deserving and the undeserving. People from outside said that she was imposed upon, that she was surrounded by spongers and hoaxers. But it did not matter to her any more than it did to Alex when he gave money to those who begged for it. It was not for her to judge; it lay between the recipient and Almighty God.

Mary Hughes was practising Christian Socialism as her father and his friends had spoken of it. The practice was not so wonderful as it might be in theory, except for the spirit of Mary Hughes herself. But it was dramatic enough, at a time when millions were haunted by the misery of the Means Test, for Bee Kay to write a sensational feature article on Mary Hughes and the Dewdrop Inn without too gross a distortion of the facts. The Features Editor was pleased. Bee Kay was personalizing the slump, reducing a world depression to the manageable proportions of a sob story. He wanted more.

Bee Kay racked her brains. At the Dewdrop Inn there had been talk of an admiral who had taken Holy Orders. He was working as Chaplain to the Sailors' Home. There were possible angles. Admiral saves A.B.'s Soul.

The Features Editor did not think much of it. But Bee Kay was working on space. "You can have a go," he said; "it's Christmas. We may be slack. But it sounds pretty thin to me."

It was very thin. What happened is not at all precise. Bee Kay gave to Father Williamson and to me a series of different versions of what happened. They were all vivid, but all as might be expected after a lapse of so many years inconsistent with one another and with the facts as remembered by other people as well or better qualified to speak. Exactly what happened has become even more vague as a result of Bee Kay's various accounts than it was before. But the really important element in the story can be accepted without any doubt.

Bee Kay tried to interview Alex, and Alex would have nothing to do with her. He had as great a distrust of the Press as his beloved Jellicoe and he was horrified at the idea that he should discuss with any journalist the motives which had led to his taking orders. He fobbed the wretched woman off by sending her to see Edyth.

(Here we have an interesting example of the divergence between Bee Kay's evidence and that of others. Bee Kay said that she saw Edyth Woods at the Vicarage, and when the Vicar and others swore she had never stayed at the Vicarage, she emended this to "somewhere close to the Vicarage". She was most emphatic that Edyth was staying in the East End. There is no reason why she should be mistaken, and yet everyone is emphatic that Edyth never came up to London. She was too blind to be able to. Bee Kay certainly saw Edyth, but she does not remember blindness, only a difficulty of movement. All of which proves nothing more than the difficulty of relying upon memory.)

From Edyth, Bee Kay tried to discover details of Alex's conversion. It is an axiom of journalism that no admiral could become a clergyman without undergoing some violent conversion. Edyth assured Bee Kay that there was no violent conversion as far as she knew. It was a very unproductive interview. Bee Kay failed to secure the christian name by which the family knew him or the nickname by which he was known in the Navy or the correct way to spell Riall. All she elicited was the information that the Padre had won a D.S.O. as Fleet Signals Officer during the Battle of Jutland. There could be no harm, Edyth thought, in passing on information like that. No malice or stupidity could get that wrong.

Bee Kay was very disappointed. She was impressed by the religious service, which she would like to have described plainly and simply. But if she did so, she knew that her copy would go into the wastepaper basket. Here was just a simple beautiful service in a nearly empty church. That wasn't news.

Then she got the "handle". Signals Officer. Gets signal from the Almighty to serve God. During the Battle of

Jutland! That would be better still. But how did he get it? In morse? By radio? Semaphore? Very tricky, unless one finds the right ambiguity. Intercepted message? Too factual. What about "interposed"? That would sound as though it meant something and yet commit her to nothing at all. "An interposed signal which, his sister told me, came from no Earthly Captain, but from a Higher Command'." The whole story could be hung from that. She wondered whether it was too corny. But she decided No. In her humble way she was learning the lesson which across the Channel Adolf Hitler was teaching Dr Goebbels. People will believe any lie provided that it is big enough. What made the lie so convincing was that it did not contain a vestige of the truth. It was not an exaggeration or a distortion. It was a pure lie.

The Features Editor printed the article, but there were protests from two members of the staff. One, a Roman Catholic, said that it could not be true, as acolytes officiated only in the Roman Catholic Church. The second, an Anglo-Catholic, said that Bee Kay could never have attended the service as she had got the vestments wrong. But nobody suggested that this was not the mysterious way in which God moved.

Bee Kay's confession explained how the lie came to be told, but it left two questions unanswered, "Why did Alex not protest at the time?" and "Why did he say to Lettice, 'Well it was no earthly command'?"

From Stride I knew that the publication of the story had made Alex very angry. But what was the point of protesting? The newspaper, if it printed the rebuttal of the story, would distort it in some way in order to avoid the blame. The young woman would get into trouble. Other newspapers would take the story up. There would be no end to the publicity.

161

When his anger had passed, Alex probably felt a pity for Bee Kay, not just because she had told a lie, but because the lie which she had told was a blasphemy against the Holy Spirit. Rather than protest to the newspaper against her, Alex probably prayed that she would realize the sin she had committed against the Holy Ghost and repent of it.

From her first letter to Father Williamson it was plain that Bee Kay did repent of this as the shabbiest act in her journalistic career without ever analysing why.

On receiving her letter, Father Williamson wrote back that it was possible that Bee Kay had written truer than she thought. After all, what other explanation was there for the mysterious remark to Lettice?

This remark of Father Williamson's struck me as an echo of what I myself had said to him when I went round with Boston to the Vicarage. It was a theory I had worked on until I reached the conclusion that when Alex said to his niece that it was "no earthly command", he was referring not to any incident during the Battle of Jutland, but to his call to take Holy Orders.

I looked back at Bee Kay's first letter and I saw to my astonishment that Father Williamson had already received that letter when Boston and I visited him. He had said not a word about it, but apparently had immediately written putting the proposition to her that she had, by some sort of divine inspiration, stumbled upon the truth.

She violently repudiated the idea. From the amount she quoted from the Bible, it was clear that she had studied it deeply and she used her texts to reprove Father Williamson for what she obviously conceived as a plot to suppress the truth about her lie, in order to get a film made about Padre Woods.

From a third letter it was plain that Father Williamson had denied the accusation and re-asserted that she might in fact have stumbled on the truth. One could see Bee Kay wrestling with her conscience and her sense of reality; and then suddenly she had been taken with the idea and produced a wonderful suggestion that the flashes of the guns should spell out to the astonished Alex "Feed my sheep", in morse!"

The correspondence was one-sided; but from what Bee Kay had written, the case looked very black against the Vicar of St Paul's, Dock Street. Why hadn't he immediately told Boston and myself that he had heard from Bee Kay that the whole story was a newspaper ramp? Why had he tried to persuade Bee Kay that the lie she had confessed to really wasn't a lie? There seemed no other explanation than a deliberate policy to mislead us.

I was appalled at what had happened. Ultramontane Films Inc. would have to be notified. From their point of view, the deal would be off. Boston and I would be accused of bad faith and if we tried to exculpate ourselves, the wretched Williamson would be liable to prosecution, wouldn't he, for *suppressio veri*, obtaining money under false pretences or something equally sordid.

Then it occurred to me that if Williamson had deliberately planned to suppress the truth about the "interposed message", it was fantastic that he should have handed over to me the evidence of his guilt. He was an absent-minded man, but he wouldn't have forgotten a thing like that.

I went to St Paul's Vicarage and Father Williamson greeted me with the warmth of utter innocence. "What can I do for you, old man?"

I explained.

He was amazed. "But I told you that afternoon with Boston," he said. "And then *you* said there must be something in it, because of what the Padre had told Lettice."

"You couldn't possibly have told me," I said. "If you had, Boston and I would have packed the whole thing in immediately."

"But I could swear I did," he answered. "I told you and I told Lettice. That's how I knew the Padre had told her that it was 'no earthly command'. She couldn't understand why he had said that, if it was all a pack of lies."

I suddenly saw a possible explanation. Father Williamson was so distracted that he had thought he had told us, but it had been only in his mind to tell us and we had unconsciously sidetracked him. "If what you say is true," I said, "Lettice will confirm it."

I rang her up. "Of course Father Williamson told me," she answered.

"Then why didn't you tell *me*?" I asked.

"Because you *knew*," she answered. "You had been to see Father Williamson and you came along full of this theory that something had happened, though not what Bee Kay said; and it made sense."

"So it's really all my fault?" I said.

"Why should it be anyone's fault?" she asked. "Perhaps this was the way it was meant to be."

I put down the receiver. It was a fantastic suggestion that this ridiculous comedy of errors was all part of a divine plan. One could maintain that God wished a book to be written about Alex, that the lie should be exposed and the truth publicly proclaimed, that this would not have been possible if Boston and I had discovered at the beginning what I now knew. That was all perfectly conceivable, provided that the God in whom Alex believed really existed.

But there was an insuperable objection to the theory.

"If it were true," I said to Father Williamson, "it would mean that God was commercially dishonest. He's trying to swindle Ultramontane Films Inc."

164

"How do *you* know?" asked Father Williamson.

"Well, isn't he?" I said. "There is absolutely nothing I have discovered that could possibly make a film."

"Have you found anything in the Padre's life which might show the Divine Purpose?" he asked.

I told him about the breaking off of Phyllis Sealey's engagement and the discovery of the muscular atrophy. "But it might be pure chance."

"It must have taken the Padre years to realize why his engagement fell through, but it didn't shake his faith in God."

"I haven't got any faith in God," I said, seeing where he was trying to take the argument.

"And yet even you have noticed that the way this book has gone so far is not natural; the film company believing that story, the two different people picking you for the job of writing it, and then this misunderstanding—I tell you, this book is meant to be written."

"But it doesn't make sense," I said. "Can *you* make sense of it?"

"I'm not writing the book," he answered. "You're the person who'll have to make sense of it. I've arranged for you to meet Margaret Earler. See her. See some of the other people he knew. Perhaps it's here in the East End that the clue to the whole thing lies."

"I ought to tell Ultramontane Films what has happened," I said.

"Why not?" he said. "If God wants this book written, it won't make any difference. Not from the way things have gone so far."

"When can I see Margaret Earler?" There was something in his voice, a conviction, that made me decide to take the book one stage further before I notified my New York agent. "If I can see her tomorrow, I'll stay at the Red Ensign overnight."

"Do that," he said. "I'll fix it." He took me to the door and shook me by the hand. "You know, I envy you," he said.

I did not know what he meant, then.

CHAPTER ELEVEN

I SPENT that evening with Dr Bullitt, the Beloved Physician, as Alex nicknamed him, or B.P. for short.

He lives about seven minutes' walk from the Red Ensign Club up Leman Street, which is really the northern continuation of Dock Street. It is a busy thoroughfare down which the heavy lorries clatter to the docks or across Tower Bridge from Aldgate East. A hundred years ago it was a street where merchants lived above their warehouses. Today most of the old houses have gone and in their place are either towering warehouses and office-blocks or blitz-sites with loosestrife in the cracks of cellar floors. The Doctor's house is an anomaly, as is the Doctor himself. Both belong to the nineteenth century.

He was born in this house and has lived there all his life. His father was the Doctor of Leman Street before him and it was he who converted the downstairs store-room into a surgery and waiting-room. The waiting-room has plate-glass windows like a shop, but these are painted up to eye-level so that no one can see in. The entrance to the house is at the side, a narrow passage and steep stairs mounting to the drawing-room, first floor front, and the dining-room behind it.

It is rather strange coming in to this drawing-room from the cobbled street outside, not because the room is different from thousands of other middle-class drawing-rooms, but because it is so different from the interiors of the little cottages and vast working-class tenements which surround it. It is comfortable; a bright fire blazes in the hearth; and there is a great feeling of calm. Those who are sensitive to the moods of places would say that nobody had quarrelled in that room for many years.

Not that Dr Bullitt is an even-tempered man. He can be peppery about the Health Scheme and the Welfare State and other things which try to do for everyone by law what he and those like him did for some from a sense of love and loyalty. But he does not quarrel. He talks and he argues and he tells long stories, in the labyrinths of which he sometimes gets lost, but he always find his way out safely in the end, if necessary by saying, "Well, to cut a long story short . . ."

Father Groser has a story of going to see Dr Bullitt because he wasn't feeling well. The waiting-room was crowded but when Dr Bullitt saw Father Groser he said, "Oh, hullo, you're just the person I want to see." Dr Bullitt took him into his consulting-room and talked to him at great length on a matter of burning interest and at last Father Groser looked at his watch. "Well, I shall have to be going now," he said; and that was the end of the consultation.

On the other hand, Father Groser has other stories of the Doctor spending whole nights with men and women seriously ill, absolutely devoted and absorbed, oblivious of everything else but their survival. A dedicated man.

I had formed an idea of what Alex's old friend Dr Bullitt was like. He was broadly built, rather below average height, bluff, white-haired and very devout. I found him rather over average height, thinly built with a tendency to obesity, shy (with a slight hesitation in his speech), not even a grey hair on his head and only in a most general way religious. "I never imagined I could be friends with a parson," he said; "yet meeting the Padre was the greatest experience of my life."

The Doctor was exactly the opposite of Father Williamson. He thought carefully before he spoke, understated rather than overstated and was as precise in his judgments of people as he would be in a diagnosis.

I liked him immensely both for the gusto of his life and the calm within which it was enclosed. He had with him two lady assistants, Miss Last and Miss Langhorne, both of them grey-haired, gentle, ministering and with different functions in the household. Seeing them together, I could see how different they were. But I could never tell which was which when they were apart. Perhaps the similarity of the initials was confusing. Perhaps it was that after working for so long with Dr Bullitt they were both so much more like one another than they were like anybody else. One of them looked after the dispensary and the other looked after the house; but both of them looked after the Beloved Physician with such unobtrusive devotion that I never could and never shall be able to sort them out.

They and, for most of Alex's time, the Doctor's devoted sister were all gliding about the house. I use the word "glide" deliberately, because they did not appear to walk. The door would open noiselessly and I would look up and there would be Miss Last (or Miss Langhorne) perched on an easy chair, as though she had flown in with the tea-tray loaded with home-made cakes, a dove of domestic peace.

In my crude reporter's way I tried to get facts from them all, something which had happened, a problem, an event, a little drama. But the magnificent thing was that nothing had happened. Nothing remained in their minds so important as Sunday lunch: (the Padre's soup-plate, glass and coffee-cup not filled as full as others, because with the weakness in his hands he was afraid of spilling liquids), the roast sirloin of beef and Yorkshire pudding, the apple tart; during the meal a lazy conversation, sometimes funny, often trivial, but always relaxed. After luncheon coffee was flown into the drawing-room and for a time they talked about things that they had talked about before, about Edyth and Alex going to church in one of his cars (all of which vehicles were disastrous) and in this one he ran off the road into a field and abandoned it; or the time when he had taken his hat off because his brow was covered in sweat and a negro put a penny in the upturned hat thinking he was a beggar. Stories were repeated over and over again and by the time a story had become a chestnut, it had reached the peak of eminence. It was like being awarded the Order of Merit.

Sometimes Alex talked about somebody in whom he was interested. Sometimes Dr Bullitt talked about some case which puzzled him. On other occasions B.P. was called out on a case. But ideally, not long after the coffee was finished, these two hard-worked men closed their eyes and went fast off to sleep, while the ministering angels flew the dishes upstairs and washed them up.

I could understand Alex's attraction to the Doctor's household. After a week of rowdiness, which perhaps had culminated in a Saturday night when there were more drunks than all the other nights in the week, and all the other executive officers had gone home for the week-end, he had only to walk down Leman Street and he was in a world which was very like his Alverstoke home in its simplicity and gentleness. There was no need to talk unless he wished, no fear of suddenly being interrupted by someone appealing for help, no feeling that he had to be bright and entertaining. He was more at home there during the last twenty years of his life than he was anywhere on earth.

When he took his holidays, he would go to stay with his brother Charles at Alverstoke, and later on when he grew too infirm, with Hugh and Eucharis at East Bergholt. But there was a feeling of constraint between them, at least during the first few days. They felt that Alex was set in a habit of asceticism, which was uneasy in their comfortable homes. They sensed something which they thought was disapproval, but perhaps was merely Alex's difficulty in readjusting himself. After a week the constraint went and they were as good friends as ever.

The physical merit of the B.P.'s house in Leman Street was that it was geographically in Dockland, a little middle-class sanctuary which was yet part of the place and the life to which the Padre was dedicated. There was no constraint.

Alex did not cut himself off from his family. He was in fact the centre of the family circle. Brothers and sisters, cousins, nephews and nieces were kept together because he kept in touch with them all. According to Hugh's daughter, Valerie, he was not very interested when things were going well. But he had an uncanny instinct for trouble. If one of the family was very hard up, a letter would arrive from Alex, containing a cheque. If one of them was ill, he would be the first to visit the hospital. By going to the East End, he did not cut himself off from his old life. By correspondence he retained friendships dating right back to his childhood.

But all the same he seems to have been conscious of a clash between the world of Dock Street and the world outside. He very seldom visited parts of London west of Aldgate pump. And with the exception of Lettice Woods, he did not welcome visits of his family to the Red Ensign Club. If one of them came to London and wanted to see him, he would arrange to meet them in Cannon Street underground station. There they would sit on a bench in the Tube, talking while the trains roared in and out of the station.

I tried to extract from Dr Bullitt dramatic stories of the work which Alex had done in the East End. But it was no use. "He wasn't dramatic," the Doctor said. "The things he did were very simple, unobtrusive things."

"Such as what?"

"Say a man was suffering from T.B., the Padre would get him into hospital. He needed a bed and he hadn't any money. He'd given him the money and if he couldn't get into the Sailors' Home, he'd find somewhere for him. He had a wonderful circle of friends. He enjoyed pulling the strings to help people. He worked a great deal with Alcoholics Anonymous on dipsomaniac cases. Stride can tell you more about that than I can. You see, the Padre and I were both very busy; and of course we did work together in some cases. But the great thing between us was that we relaxed together."

I asked if that was confined to the Sunday luncheon.

"Oh, no," he said. "Every year we would go to the Royal Tournament together. If I was free, I might take him on a visit to some hospital. I remember once I took him to see a man in a mental hospital. We walked down long corridors and through wards and suddenly a man came up to us and said, 'Which of you is the undertaker?' The Padre and I looked at one another, not certain whether he was a patient or one of the staff. Then I said, 'Neither of us is the undertaker. We're both his assistants.' The Padre loved that.

"Then sometimes we went to funerals together. He much preferred funerals to marriages. I remember once I drove him out to one of the cemeteries, for the funeral of one of his old shipmates. Everything was going all right, until the clergyman said, 'this our dear sister departed.' The Padre turned to me and grinned. 'Wrong one,' he said and picked up his hat."

As the Doctor talked of Alex, he kept smiling and giving sudden little laughs, like a kettle boiling over. There was no sense of talking of a *dead* man. He spoke as one does of someone dearly loved, who may at any moment walk into the room. I remarked on this and the Doctor said, "I don't feel he has gone. He is very close all the time. I have no feeling of sorrow. He's far too alive for that."

"You mean, vivid as a memory?"

He hesitated. "It's very hard to disentangle subjective impressions," he said. "One's always liable to read one's own beliefs into them. I can tell you that as a doctor I don't see how the soul can survive after the body has ceased to live. So I would be inclined to say that it is just a vivid memory. But it doesn't feel like that. It feels like a spiritual presence quite outside myself."

I had assumed that the Doctor had shared Alex's religious beliefs; but it now came out that he didn't. They had never talked of religion. "I think the Padre thought that if I wanted to talk about it, I would. But I didn't, because his faith was so simple I was afraid my doubts might shake it." The Doctor disapproved of much of the Padre's practice, the ritualistic approach to religion for example, and Alex's rushing along in the middle of the night to one of the maternity hospitals in order to baptize new-born babies that were not expected to live. "I can't believe that the Almighty would hold it against a new-born babe that it hasn't been sprinkled with Holy Water," he said, "and it used to make me angry to think of Alex turning out in all weathers, when he was a sick old man."

I came back to the possibilities of drama in the Padre's life. "What about the late war?" I asked, "surely during the blitzes . . .?

"It wasn't dramatic," the Doctor answered. "Of course he was tireless and magnificent. Mr Weekes, the Vicar, wasn't able to do much of the shelter work. His housekeeper was even older than he and was very frightened. But the Padre was in his element. All the Admiral in him came out. He was quite literally fearless, because he believed that he would be killed only if God wanted him to be. He only wore a tin hat as a good example to other people. Night after night he would stomp through the streets, going from shelter to shelter, making friends with the people, whatever their race or creed. He'd quieten them down, say a little prayer and move on to the next."

"At least the blitz was dramatic," I suggested, feeling that Dr Bullitt was playing the old English game of understatement.

"Of course. But the strength of the Padre was that he wasn't. You can say that even in peacetime he was surrounded with people whose lives were intensely dramatic, dope-addicts, neurotics whose home life was a mess, drunkards, the sick, the dying, the mentally unstable. *Their* lives were dramatic enough, but the way in which the Padre impinged on those lives was very undramatic— and anyway he was usually just a link in a chain. For example, I remember one shelter we both went to. It wasn't an official shelter; in fact it was less safe than many of the houses, just a railway arch. But the people *felt* safe there. They collected under it and made it a shelter.

"The Padre and I used to visit it and I remember one evening he said, 'You know, B.P., these people would feel much better if they had a cup of tea. We ought to get them some.'

"It wasn't very far from the Red Ensign Club. So he went to see Coleman, who was the Chief Steward— you must meet him by the way, he's retired and is running a pub, but he'll give you a different slant on the Red Ensign Club from the one you'll get from Stride. Coleman would do anything for the Padre and he laid on hot tea at night and again in the morning before the people left the shelter. They made great urns of it and carried it across from the club.

"Of course it meant obtaining an extra tea-ration from the Food Office. But Coleman fixed that. He rang up the Food Office and said, 'I'm speaking for Admiral

Woods.' If he'd said, 'I'm speaking for the Chaplain of the Red Ensign Club,' they wouldn't have taken any notice. But 'the Admiral' worked like a charm." (I found out later from Coleman that Alex was quite worldly in the use of his rank to get what he wanted. "Use the Admiral if you think it's necessary," he would say to Coleman with a grin.)

Dr Bullitt went on, "There was nothing very heroic or dramatic about getting those people a warm drink morning and evening. And it wasn't very difficult to do, once somebody had thought of it. But the point is, it was the Padre who thought of it. It had never occurred to me. Multiply that incident by a thousand, ten thousand, and you have the Padre's pastoral ministry. But of course you haven't got a film."

"You haven't got a book either," I said. I felt defeated by the elusiveness of my man. He had said nothing which anybody could remember, written nothing which anyone thought worth preserving and done nothing which was really spectacular.

"It wasn't what he did or said," said the Doctor, reading my thoughts, "it was what he *was*."

"A very holy man. A man of God. But what is that?" I asked. "To me it's something utterly incomprehensible, a sort of beneficent aberration."

"No," said the Doctor, "it wasn't an aberration. He was the sanest man I ever met—and one of the most matter-of-fact."

An idea recurred to me. "Would it be possible to show him reflected in the lives of other people? To take some typical stories and show how the Padre helped those in distress. Did he convert anyone, for instance?"

"If he had, he would never have spoken of it."

All the same it was worth trying. There had been a long document which Father Williamson had handed me, from a young sailor, called *The Padre and I*. It was useless from my point of view, because the young man had been a Christian to start with, the great change wrought by the Padre was merely a conversion to Anglo-Catholicism, the story of how a good young man in one way became a good young man in another way. But there must be others more interesting or startling, whom Stride, Badham or others could tell me about.

It was time for me to go. "I'd like to show you one of the big shelters," said the Doctor. "I'll walk back with you to the Club."

We went out into the wide cobbled street. The heavy daytime traffic was over. There was not a single vehicle in the roadway. But on the pavements there were people walking, leaning against walls, talking; two vividly blonde girls with clackety high heels either side of a zoot-suited African or West Indian, a knot of Jews arguing prices of something at the street corner. Compared with the bright room from which we had come, it all seemed desolate.

The Doctor took me up a side-street. "Of course, it would be closed now," he said, "but you must see it in daylight tomorrow."

"I'm lunching with Stride," I said. "Could I come after lunch, before I see Margaret Earler?"

"Yes," he said. "Yes, that would be good. I'm glad you're seeing Margaret. The Padre was very fond of her."

"Tell me about her."

I thought that he had not heard me, because he said nothing. The soot-black buildings were invested with a sort of dignity by night; or rather than dignity, a sense of mystery. "No," said the Doctor, "I'd prefer you to tell me."

Later he added. "But she is very remarkable."

We came into Cable Street. The lights were still on in the pubs and the snack-bars. Foreign voices were raised, but I could not tell whether in anger or argument. Outside a bar a figure muffled in a coat tattered and filthy barred our path. " 'Evening, Doctor." Under a scarecrow hat was a face overgrown with a tangle of hair, through which two bloodshot eyes looked out, like a ferret from a heather bush.

I looked at Dr Bullitt, expecting to see annoyance or disgust written on his face. But he was smiling with delight.

"Oh hallo, Admiral!" he said. "I haven't seen you for weeks. I thought they'd put you away."

The old rogue muttered something. His eyes gleamed as he saw the Doctor feel in his pocket. The beggar's hand shot out and took the silver coin. "Good night, Doctor," he said. "God blesh you."

As he reeled off, I said, "A rival admiral?"

"The Padre loved him," he said. "How old would you say he was?"

"As old as gin," I said.

"It's not gin," said the Doctor. "It's red biddy." He chuckled. "He's never been to sea, except maybe one voyage as a deckhand. And he's only in his fifties. That beard is part of his stock-in-trade. Once he was ill and went to hospital. When he came out he was clean shaven and they'd burnt his clothes in the incinerator and they gave him a new rig-out. He was furious. He could reduce his clothes to rags but it took months for the beard to grow."

I found it hard to imagine Alex, who had run the *Topaze* as if it was a seminary, accepting this old rogue without disapproval.

The Doctor shrugged. "He's incorrigible," he said; "what can you do except slip him a bob? After all, who does he harm except himself?"

We walked up the street to the Red Ensign Club. "I've enjoyed tonight," the Doctor said.

"So have I," I said. I did not seem to have advanced much in my search, at least in any of the directions I had expected. But there had been a repose, a contentment, in the Doctor's house, which had refreshed me.

"I say," said the Doctor and then stopped.

"Yes?"

"When this is over, I mean when you've finished your research, I'd like it if we could go on seeing one another."

The suggestion took me completely by surprise. I had enjoyed the Doctor's company, so it was not unnatural that he had enjoyed mine. That was not the reason for surprise. It was something which only rose to my consciousness when the Doctor made this offer of friendship. Until that moment I had assumed that Alex and I would not have liked one another, that we would have had nothing in common and he would probably have disapproved of me. Yet his greatest friend had said that he would like to see me after the book was finished. Of course it might mean that I appealed to the non-Alex side of his nature. On the other hand it could mean that at least in the Leman Street drawing-room we could have met and laughed and liked one another. After all he had a place in his heart for the red-biddy Admiral.

I took the Doctor's hand. "I should like it very much," I said.

CHAPTER TWELVE

THE bar of the Red Ensign Club was still open and I bought a drink. "Did you know the Padre?" I asked the barman.

"A fine man," said the barman, "too good a man for this place."

I asked what he meant.

"They said he was a saint when he died," said the barman, "but they didn't go to chapel when he was alive. Just a handful did. But the rest of them sponged on him with their hard luck stories. The money he gave away— for nothing. He couldn't resist a bum." He wiped the counter. "Of course he came down here each morning and read some prayers. Most of 'em like that, though they didn't say so. But he never got them into church; not unless they went at home anyway."

I remembered the conversation I had had that morning with an Australian and a Dane, who were two of the Padre's regulars. Both of them admired him as a good and holy man. But neither had been brought up as an Anglo-Catholic. The Dane had been baptized a Lutheran and a Lutheran he still was. They were both religious men, but curiously they spoke of attending his chapel in order to please the Padre, not in order to worship God. It was a tribute to his personality, such as the welfare officer, Badham, had said when he said. "It didn't matter what the Padre believed. It was his personality that was important."

I tried to bring the discussion back to this question.

How was it that a man so universally acknowledged as holy commanded so little respect for his beliefs?

But the old Dane—the Grand Old Man of the Red Ensign Club, who had begun to patronize it long before Alex ever went there—could not hold to a topic like that. "I am Lutheran," he said. "Twice I am shipwrecked. Three times torpedoed. Still I am alive." The wonder of his survival dazzled him to all else. I wondered if Lazarus, after he was raised from the dead, had been similarly obsessed.

Standing in the bar, sipping my warm beer, I pondered this strange phenomenon. The B.P., whose friendship with the Padre was the greatest experience in his life, had not altered his beliefs by an iota after twenty years of friendship.

Clearly Alex had a pure goodness that not even the most critical could undermine. I remembered that Moberly had told me that he was the most integrated person he had ever met. His goodness had to be acknowledged, even by people who held quite different beliefs. Badham, for example, and as I later found out, Coleman, the steward, a pragmatic Labour Party man, who believed in looking after the bodies and letting the souls look after themselves.

As the lieutenant whom he had reproved for bad language, had said, Alex was "not a Bible-thumper". Yet wasn't it a criticism of him as a priest that he had failed to convince others of the God, Who was the source of his holiness?

Coleman and Badham, who had known Alex well, were content to regard him as a good man who happened to believe in God. In that case he did not interest me. He just happened to be genetically lucky and as I should never have the chance of meeting him the whole research would be as elusive as entering a room filled with the scent of a beautiful woman who had left, never to return.

Yet Badham that morning had said to me, "Of course the Padre is still here. He's running the place." And when I asked Stride (perhaps to be discounted, because he was a believer), he answered," Naturally." And Bullitt, though he could not believe in survival as a doctor, thought that the sense of Alex's presence was not just due to the vividness of memory.

I ordered another drink, before the barman closed the shutters. "Tell me," I said, "do you feel the Padre's still around?"

"I'm always expecting him to come through that door," he answered.

Not a beneficent aberration, Bullitt had said. The Padre was matter-of-fact.

I drank my beer and went up to my cabin-like room. I felt a temptation to kneel beside the bed to ask God, if he existed, or Alex, if he was around, for guidance. But I did not believe in God and if I prayed for help to the man whose life I was supposed to be writing, I would be the sorriest sort of ass.

By next morning my mood had changed and I started to work along a different line. The reactions which I had had on my first visit to the Sailors' Home were very subjective. They had no relation to what Alex himself felt or to what sailors would feel, landing in London and faced with alternative accommodation in the district.

It was also unfair to judge the Sailors' Home entirely by modern standards. The great new building which was being erected in Dock Street would have to be judged by those standards, but the central block and the renovated building on Ensign Street belonged to earlier periods. At the moment the Ensign Street entrance was the main entrance; but when the new building on Dock Street was finished, it would revert to a back entrance.

I reflected on the inflexibility of bricks and mortar for the expression of good intentions. A building is planned and constructed to advance the welfare of one generation, and as needs change and standards are raised the existence of the building retards the welfare of the generations to come.

I spent some hours in trying to understand the history of the Sailors' Home in relation to the neighbourhood. It emerged as a complicated little story of the sort which probably bored Alex, but to me is interesting.

What is now roughly the Parish of St Paul's, Dock Street, was an odd pocket of land, outside the limits of the City of London and not included in the County of Middlesex. Until 1688 it was controlled as a suburb by the City of London. In that year King James II detached Well Close Precinct, or Tower Ground as it was also called, and included it in the Liberties of the Tower of London.

The Tower was responsible for maintaining law and order. It appointed magistrates, who, sitting with the Governor of the Tower, tried all persons accused of treason, felony and minor crimes. It held a Court of Record and Request for the recovery of small debts.

A court house and a prison were built in Well Close and they continued in use until 1830. The prison was then pulled down but the court house is still standing in the middle of the south side of Well Close Square, now the office of a merchant.

Enclosed by this square was a garden in which was the well which gave its name to the Close and their water to the householders. Most of the householders were connected with the sea, either foreign merchants or sea captains and their families. In consequence, it was also known in the seventeenth century as Marine Square.

At this time a poet could still call the River Thames "sweete" or "silver". Market gardens crept up to the edge of the city and at night the stars were not hidden by fog, smoke-laden. Well Close Precinct was a prosperous place, where despite the proximity of the port a good man might live with his family without fear of their being abused. A number of Danish merchants settled in the Precinct and at the end of the seventeenth century King Christian V of Denmark built a church at his own expense in Marine Square, neighbouring the well. The architect was the Danish sculptor, Caius Gabriel Cibber, whose son the poet-dramatist, Colley Cibber, died in London, was buried in Westminster Abbey and is preserved in the invective of Alexander Pope.

I wandered through the square, even in its desuetude a place of gentle charm, and immediately noted on the west side of the house that was the Danish Embassy, distinguished from its neighbours in the terrace by two afterthoughts in bas-relief, cherubs indulging in obscure play meant to symbolize the Arts and the Sciences. The house wears them today as an old lady, come down in the world, sports the bald furs which were the advertisement of her youthful fortune.

As centuries passed and the trade of London grew, the commerce of shipping usurped the orchards and the market gardens. Warehouses and stockrooms, offices, shops, pubs, brothels, dosshouses and workers' cottages sprouted from the fields. The pleasant harmony of Well Close Square was threatened by the strident growth of the docks.

But there was one development which had nothing to do with the port. It was due to the anomalous position of Well Close Precinct, so near to the City of London but not under its jurisdiction.

A censorship act was passed in 1737, which forbade the performance in London or Middlesex of any "legitimate" plays except at the "patent theatres" of Covent Garden and Drury Lane.

For years no one thought of challenging this barbarous restriction of the drama. But in 1785 an actor called John Palmer, who had made a name for himself at Drury

Lane, had an ingenious idea for evading the law. If he built a theatre in Well Close Precinct, outside the jurisdiction of London and Middlesex, he could present five-act plays for a London audience and break the monopoly of the patent theatres.

He realized that there would be strong opposition and he tried to enlist his allies with the very laying of his foundation stone. On it he inscribed the following:

The ground selected for the purpose being situated within the Liberty of His Majesty's Fortress and the Palace of the Tower of London, it has been resolved that in honour of the Magistrates and Military Officers and the Inhabitants of the said Fortress and Palace, the edifice when erected shall be called

THE ROYALTY THEATRE

Few foundation stones have so canvassed for support; perhaps because few have so needed it. There was the public, Palmer was convinced, but to reach it he needed the favour of the King, which might be enlisted by his officers in the Tower. Further to placate the authorities, he gave the proceeds of the first performance to charity. On 20 June 1789 the Royalty Theatre opened with a performance of *As You Like It*, with David Garrick's *Miss in her Teens* as a curtain-raiser. It was a great success.

Next day the patentees of Covent Garden and Drury Lane appealed to the Lord Chamberlain. He ruled in their favour and the Royalty Theatre was closed down.

It was reopened under licence for the performance of pantomimes, interludes and variety acts, but it had a chequered career. Palmer kept trying to slip in legitimate plays on the sly and was fined heavily by the Tower Magistrates for doing so. Yet when he fulfilled the baser requirements licensed by the Lord Chamberlain, he was harassed by the Society for the Suppression of Vice.

For twenty years the Royalty Theatre struggled on under various managements. Then it was renamed the

East London Theatre, in recognition of what it had really been from the start.

In April 1826 it was burnt down. But within seven months another theatre had been erected on the site, an ambitious edifice with a façade in imitation of the opera house of San Carlo. Another bid for the favour of the ruling house was made by calling it the Royal Brunswick.

It opened successfully with a dramatic performance of Sir Walter Scott's *Bride of Lammermoor*, entitled *The Mermaiden's Well or The Fatal Prophecy*.

Unfortunately the structure of the new theatre was as unstable as the late King's reason. Four days later, during a rehearsal of *Guy Mannering*, one of the walls collapsed. The great iron roof fell in. Twelve of the cast were crushed to death and many more were injured. The Royal Brunswick was a tangled mass of lath and plaster, bricks and girders, a ruin far too costly for any stage-struck financier to clear.

That was the end of the theatre, but only the beginning of the venture which concerns us.

Living in Well Close Square and witnesses of this appalling disaster in the neighbouring Well Street were many respectable people connected with the sea, who were equally distressed by the decline of the district in which they lived. They were not just concerned with the fact that the amenities of a pleasant neighbourhood were being ruined by the encroachment of a variety of men and women united in the aim of parting sailors from their money as quickly as possible. If that had been all, they could easily have moved away. But they were also roused by the plight of seamen ashore.

There were two separate problems; the relief of seamen, who having served with the Royal Navy during the Napoleonic wars had been reduced to destitution in the depression which followed; and the welfare of seamen, still in work, who were assailed even before they stepped

185

ashore by an organization of crooks, which did not rest until they were reduced to a state of destitution as absolute as that of the unemployed.

Living in the liberty of Well Close was a devout sailor named Robert James Elliot, Captain, R.N. He considered that the first task was to care for the destitute, and shortly after the collapse of the Royal Brunswick Theatre, he combined with friends in the neighbourhood to take a lease on an old warehouse in Dock Street. They opened a soup-kitchen in the basement, and on the floors above straw was laid to provide dormitories for men who would otherwise have slept in doorways and under bridges.

By our standards the Destitute Sailors' Asylum must have been a grim place, cold and draughty from the outset and very soon lousy and bug-ridden. But where there is nothing, a little is much. A start had been made. The consciences of other Christians were challenged. The foundations of Seamen's Welfare had been laid.

Elliot and his friends Admiral Gambier and Lieutenant Robert Justice, R.N. knew they were only attacking the fringe of the problem. It was no good waiting until sailors were down and out. The whole system of "crimping" crews was vicious and evil; it was not going to be easy to overthrow it, because it embraced not only the ramifications of the port underworld, but shipping companies and ship's officers. How widespread it was is indicated by the definition of "a crimp" in Ogilvie's *Imperial Dictionary*, published in 1855, the year after "crimping" had been made a penal offence, as a result of agitation by men like Captain Elliot.

CRIMP: One who decoys another into naval or military service; one who, for a commission, supplies ships with seamen just before sailing; one who decoys sailors by treating, advancing money, giving goods on credit, etc., by which the dupes get deep into debt, and when well plied with liquor are induced to sign articles, and are shipped off, discovering when too late that they have been robbed of all they possessed. Crimps frequently induce sailors to desert their ships. By the Merchant Shipping Act, 1855, 237, this practice has been rendered highly penal. Crimps also entrap emigrants, taking them to low lodging houses, where they are cheated by provision merchants and others, who pay the crimps a commission on their custom.

Elliot knew that the way to attack crimping in the 1820's was first to supply an alternative system. Seamen fell victims to crimps because there was nowhere for them to sleep between ships, except in common lodging houses run by men in the crimping market. Something like the Destitute Sailors' Asylum must be started for seamen ashore, a sailors' home which would provide better food and shelter than the common lodging houses, together with the security of not being robbed, cheated and press-ganged into service.

As he passed the wrecked Royal Brunswick Theatre, daily growing more sodden and derelict, he must gradually have evolved the idea that here was his chance. No commercial contractor could afford to clear the site, but at the Destitute Sailors' Asylum there was a small army of unemployed men, spoiling for work.

He formed a committee to acquire "the site, the leasehold, the ground, the materials and the freehold and to build thereon a Sailors' Home which should be the exclusive property of the sailors for ever". Announcing one of the first meetings of the committee in *The Times* of 1 May 1829, he openly proclaimed the purpose of the Sailors' Home as the exposure and annihilation of crimping, that "nefarious and destructive system by which British and foreign seamen are ruined on the banks of the Thames".

The money was raised, but the crimps were forewarned. When work began, they were already organized. Each morning the destitute sailors marched to the site and before they started working, prayers were offered invoking God's help. It was needed. The work was carried out not merely in the teeth of ridicule, intimidation and abuse, but in spite of beatings-up and active sabotage.

The building was completed and then the battlefield moved to the streets and on to the ships themselves. Touts from common lodging houses went aboard and with drinks and promise of women tried to persuade men to choose the licence of the lodging-house rather than the security of the Sailors' Home. Many needed no persuasion. But over the bodies of others developed arguments and fights between the touts and the men from the Sailors' Home who drove to the docks to fetch the sailors' kit. The drivers were chosen specially for their strength and toughness.

The Sailors' Home grew over the years. In 1835 there were a hundred boarders and thirty years later five times as many. The Royal Brunswick site in Well Street (re-named Ensign Street) was extended through to Dock Street in a great wooden building with sleeping accommodation in cabins, as in a ship. Other services were established; a bank, a labour exchange to enable men to get fairly and without duress the jobs into which the crimps had press-ganged them.

Next to the Dock Street extension was built St Paul's Church for Seamen and the Vicarage where Father Williamson lived. And from the Church spread other activities, a school for infants and one for older children, on the site of the Danish Church in Well Close Square.

One could see in the great new building rising on Dock Street the continuation of the tradition of Captain Elliot, and in the older parts, which had depressed me, the perspective of its historic achievement. Against the background of Captain Elliot and Admiral Gambier, Alex's devotion of the last twenty years of his life to the Sailors' Home was not a remarkable or quixotic act but in the same tradition of service which had led to its foundation. Nor was his Christianity a religious element super-added. Into the very building had gone the daily prayers of the destitute. Those prayers had been forgotten by the men who used the home a hundred years later, accepting what was conceived proudly as "the exclusive property of the sailors for ever" as being something which, since it belonged to everyone in general, mattered to no one in particular. It was taken for granted, just as the Padre was taken for granted. It is a natural human tendency to value what you have less than what you want to have next. It is only when its loss is threatened that you realize the preciousness of a possession.

Stride told me that once or twice, depressed with the apathy of the men whom he had come to serve, the Padre talked of going away and finding somewhere where he could be more useful. It was only then that a sort of panic went through the Club, a realization of the preciousness of the old man who came down every morning to say a prayer or two in the canteen at 10 a.m., who would fall for any hard luck story and who would never turn a man away from his cabin, unless he was so drunk that he was violent.

Then they would go up to him and beg him to stay, and some of them would even attend his services in chapel for a little while, until the old man was submerged once more in the indifference of familiarity.

CHAPTER THIRTEEN

SITTING at Stride's table for lunch were two other members of the staff, Badham, the Welfare Officer, and the accountant. Both of these were white-haired men in their fifties, the accountant a long-headed fellow who presided over the outer office, the Welfare Officer, a small man with a deaf-aid, who functioned behind a door so near the Ensign Street entrance that you didn't notice it was there unless you already knew.

There was something Dickensian about these three administrative officers, lunching behind the half-privacy of the canteen screen. What does one mean by "something Dickensian"? Perhaps that they had sat at the same table for so long, disposing so effectively of every possible subject of conversation, except immediate shop, that it was no longer possible to say anything fresh.

Most merchant seamen today are found jobs by "the Pool"; but there are some men who are not registered with the Pool, because they suffer from some weakness, physical, mental or moral. It was Badham's task to find work for these. Before he came to the Sailors' Home, his job had consisted in finding work for discharged convicts. He had developed a fine sense of what jobs would fit what men. Employers trusted his judgment. He was impressive at work in his office, as is every man who is on top of his job.

The accountant gave me the impression of having a heart of gold, imprisoned in double entry. His greatest temptation was to be nicer than his job allowed. On him fell a series of invidious tasks. He had to tell sailors on the bum to pay their bills or quit, and sailors on the booze that they would be ejected unless they got sozzled more quietly. On his head was poured their wrath, delivered in many languages and as many instalments. A drunken man who had exhausted his obscenities would walk half-way down Ensign Street and then, thinking of a particularly mordant insult, labour back into the outer office and spit it in the accountant's face. The accountant never answered back. But there was a sort of pent-up look about him, as if he would never be able to stop if he once let himself go.

Stride had lost the reserves and hesitations of our first meeting. The Council of Management had sat on me and decided I was to be helped. All the same he was difficult to follow. The progress of his conversation was like a moorhen's; his thoughts would jerk brightly on and then suddenly disappear, leaving a trail of bubbles as a reassurance that the disappearance was not for good. Sometimes the words were audible only as a confused sound; at others each word was audible but charged with a meaning too allusive for me to understand. At these moments he would smile enigmatically. I decided that it was better to smile also, because if I asked him what on earth he meant, he might dive and not surface until I left.

I started by bringing up the question of the Padre's being a sucker for hard luck stories, always good for the price of a meal.

"There was something of the naval officer in it," Stride suggested. "He wanted to see his men were properly fed. And as they weren't on rations, the only way he could do it was to slip a man the price of a meal if he was broke."

"I think he was wrong," said the accountant.

"And so do I," Stride answered.

"There's many the argument we've had at this table," the Welfare Officer said. " 'Flinging his money away.' That's what we used to tell him. But it made no difference."

"He used to say, 'If it brings only one soul to God, then it is justified,' " Stride said. "And I'd say: 'What about the others you're turning into chronic spongers without any self-respect?' He hated their drinking but the money he gave them paid for the extra pint that made them drunk."

I sat back and listened to the argument which was just as spirited as if the Padre had only that moment given half a crown to some notorious cadge and was now sitting in the chair that I was occupying.

"Doesn't it depend on what the Padre aimed to do?" I asked. "If he was merely concerned with getting some food into the man, he could have stood over him and seen that his moneysworth was eaten."

"That's what Father Williamson does," Stride said. "There's a lot to be said for it." He dived for a time and when he surfaced he said, "Of course the Padre tried it once or twice. A man asked him for a loaf of bread and when he brought him one, the language was terrible."

"That remark of his, 'If it only brings one soul to God,' " I said, "surely that means he wasn't particularly interested whether the man had anything in his belly or not. What the Padre did was to give the man the chance of buying another pint of beer or something to eat. The money enabled the man to make a spiritual choice."

"And if he chose wrong?" Badham asked.

"I can't believe in God," I said, "but I think I understand what the Padre was doing in this case. The right choice wasn't necessarily buying a meal; it was the choice that brought a soul to God. If he went off and bought a bottle of red biddy with it, that might prove to be the right choice if it produced a sense of repentance (apart from the hangover), which woke his soul to God."

"You may be right," Stride said, "But it didn't prevent the Padre being hoaxed by plausible rascals."

"I wouldn't even call them plausible, most of them," the accountant said.

"What about Captain Scrimgeoir?"* asked Badham.

"Scrimgeoir didn't take me in," Stride said. "He didn't take any of *us* in."

"That didn't prevent the Padre insisting that we should take Captain Scrimgeoir in," said the accountant. He turned to me. "You see, the Padre had this money of his own and when he was very worked up, we knew that he'd spend every penny of it to get what was needed—what he thought was needed, rather. It forced our hands. To prevent him wasting his money—well, we had to waste ours."

"Father Williamson was taken in," Stride said, as if it was a great joke. "The Vicar and the Padre fell for him, hook, line and sinker. But of course I'm cynical. I distrusted him from the moment the Padre brought him in and said we must give him a room. I pointed out he wasn't eligible; he'd never been in the Merchant Navy."

"He really had been the Captain of a millionaire's yacht, though," said Mr Badham.

"Shades of the *Victoria and Albert*," I suggested, "a bond with the Inspector-General of Hospitals and Fleets."

"Oh, it wasn't the yachts," said Stride. "It was because he was going to commit suicide. He was so depressed."

"Out of grief for his wife," explained Mr Badham. "She was a millionaire's daughter."

"Or was it the millionaire's wife, whom he promised to console when the millionaire was dying?" asked the accountant.

* The name Scrimgeoir is fictitious.

"He consoled both of them," Stride said, "by all accounts. But not in wedlock."

"Anyway, when he started talking about his millionaire wife," said the accountant, "I asked him why he couldn't pay for a room in an hotel."

"And then of course the Padre said about the lifeboat."

Badham roared with laughter. "Of course. I'd forgotten about the lifeboat!"

Observing my perplexity, Stride explained that Captain Scrimgeoir had produced a letter from the Royal National Lifeboat Institution thanking him for the offer of fifteen thousand pounds to buy a new lifeboat and they would be pleased to call it *Hilda* in memory of his wife. He had shown the letter to the Padre, who was far too much of a gentleman to read it. Even if he had done so, he might not have noticed that the operative clause was that the Institution would be pleased to name the lifeboat *Hilda*, *if* he made a donation of fifteen thousand pounds.

"Of course he hadn't," Stride said, "but I didn't check up on that till later. Anyway, it gave the Padre a good reason why he had no money."

"Besides, he had to be here," said the accountant, "so that the Padre could help him not to commit suicide."

"Not that he was suffering from any depression," Badham commented, "so far as I could see."

"You should have seen him when I asked him to pay his bill," Stride answered; "which I did every two or three days, suicide or no suicide. That depressed him."

"He always found the money, though," said the accountant. "He knew where to lay his hand on it."

"He had Connections," Stride said, laughing. "That's what bamboozled Father Williamson. It was one of the first things the Padre did. A visit to the Vicarage to take his mind off self-destruction. They started talking about the rebuilding fund and Scrimgeoir took on new life.

The Padre was so pleased. It was good in so many ways. It would help the church and it would give poor Captain Scrimgeoir something to take his mind off his grief."

They all doubled up with laughter.

Then Badham said, "You remember the Padre sitting here telling us how Scrimgeoir said, "Haven't you tried Lloyd's, Vicar? A Seaman's Church. Think of the Insurance angle! Sober God-fearing sailors. Think of the shipwrecks avoided! It would be an investment."

When the Vicar confessed that he had not thought of Lloyd's or the insurance angle, Captain Scrimgeoir insisted, in gratitude to the Padre and the Vicar for all that they had done for him, yes, he positively insisted, on bringing his influence to bear. "I'm not unknown in shipping circles," he said modestly, "and anything I could do . . ."

The Vicar thanked him. "It would be very helpful, sometime."

"Sometime!" Captain Scrimgeoir exclaimed. "Well, there's no time like the present!" His eyes wandered round Father Williamson's study. "Just you leave it to me, my dear Vicar. All I want is a letter from you and the Admiral—a To Whom It May Concern. I mean they know *me*, but they don't know about Your Need." He found some paper with the address at the head. "Don't trouble about the words," he said. "I know about these things. All you've got to do is to sign."

Alex related this all with high enthusiasm. "An interest in life," he said. "He just wanted an interest to take his mind off things."

Next day Stride saw Father Williamson. "You know nothing about this man," Stride said, "and now you've made him your agent. What'll you do if he goes off with the money?"

"Did he?" I asked.

"He was far too smart for that," Stride said. "He came back at the end of the first day with twenty guineas."

"As an operator I salute him," said the accountant. "He received a cheque for his post-war credits, cashed it in London, took the first train to the Inland Revenue headquarters in Llandudno, and kicked up such a row about not having received his post-war credits that they gave him a second cheque. That is impudence carried to the point of genius."

I heard more about Scrimgeoir, when I called on Father Williamson, so that he could take me to the Earlers.

"He made proper fools of us, the Padre and me. We didn't worry about giving him the letter of authorization. Think of it. He kept talking of suicide. There are times in our job when you've got to trust. We didn't find out till later that the blighter, when he took the letters along to be typed, borrowed a quid from the girl behind the counter—out of her own purse. That's something I can't forgive. Swindle me. Swindle the Padre. We're fair game. We can take it. But not a poor young girl. No . . . Now where was I?"

"You were beginning to tell me how the captain shattered your illusions."

"Of course. Well, he didn't steal any church funds, not as far as I know. But comes Christmas and he says he must go down to Devonshire for the holiday. He gives me his address. Could I lend him some money for his fare? He's a bit short, but he'll be back by the New Year and then he'll have something. Well, of course I lent him some. Six or seven quid. It was the least I could do after what he'd raised for the Rebuilding Fund."

"Even though Stride insisted he was a phoney?"

"The money didn't matter," said the Vicar. "What the Padre and I were frightened of was that he was really going to kill himself. So when he didn't come back by the New Year, I was scared. I wrote to the address at Exeter and got a letter back, saying that they knew him well enough, but he hadn't been there over Christmas. I was scared. I thought he must have done it at last. So did the Padre. We pictured him dead in a long dark railway tunnel or floating in the sea. I rang up Scotland Yard, and warned them that he was missing and maybe dead." He smiled. "Two days later a bobby came round from Leman Street. They'd got the man that we called Scrimgeoir. What they wanted to know was whether I would prosecute. I didn't want to, but they said they knew of dozens of cases of his getting small sums of money under false pretences. Then I remembered he'd got those letters of authorization and so I said I would."

"And was he sentenced?"

Father Williamson laughed. "No," he said. "Scrimgeoir paid the money he owed me into court and said that the whole thing was an entire misunderstanding. And there the matter ended. Except that the Padre was very upset."

I realized this later on, when in some papers which Stride handed over to me I discovered a reference to "the sadness of a recent betrayal".

When Alex gave money to the Admiral, or to a sailor with a hard luck story, he did not expect very much. He was casting his bread upon the waters. But when Scrimgeoir imposed on him with his story of loss and contemplated suicide, it was quite a different matter. He did not mind being made a fool of. In most of his stories he appeared in the role of a clown anyway. But it struck at his confidence that he had not recognized the difference between a man contemplating suicide and a cheap crook.

As we walked round to the Earlers', I discussed with Father Williamson the problem raised at luncheon. If a man asks you for a loaf of bread, do you give him a loaf or the money to buy it, with which he may buy a drink. "*You* buy the food, I gather."

"I do," he said. He touched a man's shoulder with his hand, a transient greeting. "Can you say there's any one solution?" He nodded to a woman. "How's your husband? Better? Fine. I've got jolly little money. People are marvellous. If I'm in a fix, from somewhere there comes a fiver. But I've got to spend it right, d'you see? It isn't my own. It's a trust. But Padre had his pension. Could do what he liked with it." He smiled at an African. "If it's your own money, you can experiment with the spirit."

He was quite right. I had been trying to dramatize Alex, at the expense of Father Williamson. I had been trying to pick out Alex from other Christians and say, "All right, I will accept you, because you are exceptional."

I might have been able to do this with Father Groser, who lived down the road, or with Mary Hughes of the Dewdrop Inn, whom Dr Bullitt thought became unhinged after her sister and brother-in-law died. But I could not do that with the man whom I had been chosen to write about. He was more deficient in the qualities which make for personality than anyone I had come across. His strength, which was undoubted, came from whatever was the source of Christianity.

We came into Well Close Square. The weak sun bathed the old black bricks. The trees, their branches thick in soot, were breaking into leaves with that wonderful yellow-green which is Nature's annual protest against London.

"Margaret lives across the Square," said Father Williamson.

I remembered a suggestion which he had made months before that in order to meet the people of his parish, he ought to be present to help me. I had violently repudiated it, because I can only work alone. He pointed to the gaunt east side of the square, still a façade of beauty and grace, though nothing had been done to maintain it for years. I said nothing.

I thought, "He's going to suggest that he should stay with me just to help, and he'll be terribly upset when I say there's nothing I should like less."

"I'll take you up to her room and then I'll leave you," he said. "She'll talk more freely if you're alone."

CHAPTER FOURTEEN

THE moment we knocked on the old peeled door, a dog
started barking. It was a distant, cavernous noise which
grew louder as the animal scuttered down the hallway.
It sounded as though the dog wanted nothing better
than to sink its teeth in our calves. Frustrated of this, it
barked furiously through the letter-box.

After some minutes we heard a woman hushing the
dog. "Do be quiet. Stop making that noise." The dog
was not quiet, but the note changed from a sort of mur-
derous frenzy to a breathy bellow.

The door opened a little and about a yard above the
doorstep appeared the white face of a worried woman,
even more harassed than usual because of the difficulty
of opening the door with one hand and restraining the
dog with the other. She was a frail creature with wispy,
straight hair and a white deaf-aid in one ear.

When she saw that it was the Vicar, pleasure and embarrassment fought for supremacy in her face. Shouting
above the barking bitch (who was revealed as an amiable,
fat beast, like a noisy old hearthrug), she said that she had
just been drying Margaret's hair. Father Williamson introduced me and I said that I could easily return later, if
that would be more convenient. This assurance was
apparently all that she needed to make the present a suitable time for the visit. She invited us into the hall, which
when she closed the door was in almost total darkness, and
then she took the dog, still barking but now more as a
form of exercise than out of anger, into the kitchen at the
back of the house.

As my eyes grew accustomed to the gloom, I looked about me. It was one of the strangest slum houses I have ever seen. Though it was a large house, the Earlers were the only family living in it. Most of the rooms, they told me later, were uninhabitable and the place had been scheduled for demolition years before. It was clean, as far as I could see, and it did not have that terrible smell that some slum houses have. Nor had it been knocked about in some crude attempts at "conversion". In fact it seemed almost exactly as it had been when the prosperous merchant family living there—perhaps at the time when Dickens published *Oliver Twist* serially—had decided to move to a more salubrious neighbourhood. Since then nothing appeared to have been done to the hall and staircase, except by time and the London atmosphere. It was a landlord-made slum, the creature of neglect. It still held charm for me, because I could imagine how it had been and how it could be made over. But the Earlers, condemned to live in it as it was, hated it passionately, or rather hated the discomfort of the rooms they occupied and the damp and decay which had consolidated in the empty rooms and threatened to invade the rest.

Margaret had the front room on the first floor. The Vicar had pointed to her windows with their array of flowers. It must have been the drawing-room in the old days, a pleasantly proportioned room with large windows through which the afternoon sun streamed. It caught the scarlet of the geranium flowers and renovated the old paint on the panelled walls. It played on the covers of the narrow bed which projected from the wall between the fireplace and the window.

Father Williamson had told me that Margaret was beautiful and from the little photograph which I had seen that first day in the Padre's study I was expecting a girl with black hair. I had forgotten my colour values. The girl lying back on the pillows had long auburn hair which framed her face and fell in thick tresses to a foot below her shoulders. I have never seen such beautiful hair of that colour. The face it framed had the delicate colouring that goes with auburn hair. Its composition had the boldness and simplicity of a Botticelli. This, I saw later, was due to the fact that the bone formation of the skull was large, but her illness had thinned the flesh, so that it was stretched taut across the high cheekbones. Most startling of all were her eyes, enormous and brilliant with laughter and wonderment.

She laughed with pleasure when she saw Father Williamson, and when he introduced me she held out her hand. The fingers were very long and pitiably thin; the wrist and forearm were no thicker than a seven-year-old girl's. One could see the bones, the articulation of the muscles.

Yet these details, enumerated like that, convey nothing of Margaret Earler. She was not beautiful in a physical sense. There was no bridge to her nose. The bone had been removed in an operation. She was as emaciated as the unfortunates of Belsen. Her beauty, which was dazzling, was of the spirit. I had expected, from things which Father Williamson had told me, that I should feel pity. But no one could pity a person as calm, as happy and as joyous as Margaret.

Father Williamson took his leave and Mrs Earler came back into the room. I was rather chary about mentioning the Padre, because Father Williamson had told me that after the Padre's death Margaret could not speak of him without bursting into tears. But she began to speak of him of her own accord, telling me stories most of which I had heard before, about the negro who put a penny in the Padre's hat, and how he was driving his sister to church in a car and drove it into a field, and how he came to see her at the sanatorium in the country and lost the return half of his ticket and found it later in the band of his hat. Far from bursting into tears, she smiled and laughed most of the time that she talked of him, as everybody else did.

I remarked on this and she said. "I'm not upset any more. You see, when Padre was alive, I only saw him when he came into the room. Now he's here all the time."

We talked about Mrs Earler's deaf-aid. She had lost her hearing as a result of measles when she was a little girl. She heard very little for about forty years. Even the blitzes were quiet affairs for her. It was as if in the reign of King Edward VII she had entered a long tunnel of silence, which she did not emerge from until towards the end of his grandson's reign the National Health Scheme gave her a deaf-aid. During those forty years London had become a hideously noisy place and at first the doctor would not let her wear it in the street because of the noise. But she took it to church and tuned in there to the service. She wasn't very good at tuning in and she sometimes used to oscillate. Padre would shake his head and say, "Whistling in church again, Mrs Earler!"

Mrs Earler began to laugh at her whistling and then she told how the Padre had made fun of the old dog barking at him every time he came to the house.

At this point Mr Earler came in. He worked in a butcher's shop and as a hobby he played the organ. His harmonium was against the wall behind the door. He had played for the Padre in the chapel of the Sailors' Home and also in the church. "He had a nice voice," he said, "not very strong. Needed a little helping over the tricky bits; but a nice voice."

I asked him if he also felt that the spirit of the Padre was still around. "Oh yes," he said. "But not as close to Mum and me as to Margaret. He used to call her 'my Margaret'. Like a daughter, she was to him."

I suspected that he had come in to give me the once-over. Anyway he soon went off to cut up more meat and Mrs Earler started to tell me how much Margaret had suffered. The tuberculosis had started in the bone and there had been this operation and that to remove infected bone and put good bone in its place. It had been contained, completely cured, the doctors thought. Margaret had gone to work in the City. Then it broke out in the lungs. She dwelt on the details as though trying to bring the reality to herself, a habit of the healthy with the sick. Her voice had a melancholy, nasal fall and it persisted, oblivious of her daughter's embarrassment, detailing the cruel course of the disease.

Suddenly Margaret broke in, speaking in a voice, not harsh, but full of authority. "Mother, what I've been through is nothing compared to what the Padre suffered. Nothing!"

I looked at the old Victorian clock on the mantelshelf. I had been there half an hour. To stay longer might overtire Margaret. Anyway that one sentence of reproof had told me more about the influence of the Padre than all my other interviews put together.

I took Margaret's hand and asked her if I could come to see her again.

"I'd like it," she said, "but I must tell you that I don't think he would have liked a book written about him. He hated that sort of thing."

"You can write a book about a man who wouldn't like a book written about him. But it isn't easy." I wanted to say, "It might be a bit easier, if you prayed it would be a good book. I can't believe in that sort of thing, but you do and it might work." But I couldn't say it. It would be cheating. "Anyway, Dr Bullitt is helping me," I said.

"I know," she said. "And of course if God wants it done, the Padre would have to agree." She laughed. "But I think he'd have hated it all the same."

As I reached the door, I turned to take a last look at her. I remembered that I had heard that an ex-curate of St Paul's, Dock Street had continued to visit Margaret weekly, after he had transferred to a North London parish. It seemed strange that a man with his own cure of souls should take time to do this. But now I understood the reason for it. The ex-curate visited Margaret not to give spiritual guidance but to receive it. As I left the room, I felt that it was not she who was sick, but I.

I went down the dark stairs, at the bottom of which the fat dog was barking like fury and wagging her tail with pleasure at the same time. I could not get over the extraordinary tranquillity which possessed Margaret Earler, a very special sort of peace. I had met nothing like it. It was far more positive than resignation; it was radiant acceptance.

I said good-bye to Mrs. Earler and promised to give her warning of my next coming. "Don't worry," she said, "there's always someone here."

I thought, "Yes, and that's your Cross, old dear; and you carry it lightly."

"She's a wonderful girl," she said, "a wonderful girl."

I went down the steps and across the square. I wished that I had asked Margaret to pray for the book. I had told myself it would be cheating. But the cheat was to tell myself that. I had been afraid to. It was just cowardice.

A phrase which I had loved for years because it was so sonorous and rolled from the tongue so smoothly came into my mind, "The peace of God that passeth all understanding." That was what Margaret Earler had! It came as a tremendous shock to me that what I had always taken for a beautiful piece of seventeenth-century rhetoric was actually the precise definition of a spiritual state.

And this was clearly what Alex himself had possessed. This was one of the things which people were trying to say when they repeated over and over again, "He was a very good man." They could not say any more, because I was asking them about something which passeth all understanding.

I thought of all the people I had met during my research, the people around Alex, the Woods family, Howard Marshall, Williamson, Stride, Father Groser, Dean Moberly, Dr Bullitt—whom I remembered I was due to visit. They were all, with the possible exception of Dr Bullitt, believers in what I regarded as the Christian myth. The degrees of their intelligence varied, but they all possessed, in greater or lesser degree, that peace which was raised to such power in Margaret Earler. It was something I did not have; nor did my friends. It would be a wonderful thing to have. I felt as if I was in a shadowed country, and away across some impassable barrier, a deep chasm or unnavigable channel, I could see others in brilliant sunshine. "But I'm blowed if I'm going to commit intellectual suicide," I said. "Anyway I can't. It's not my fault if the whole Christian religion appears nonsense."

As I walked up Leman Street, I remembered an interview I had had with Prebendary Inglis, who had been Assistant Principal of Cheshunt. He made an appointment at twelve-thirty at a City of London church, where he held Holy Communion every Thursday at noon and at 1 p.m. It was a church I did not know and to be certain of being punctual, I arrived early.

It was a wonderful spring morning; the churchyard was filled with flowers and on the many benches people were sitting, letting the warm sun bathe their faces. Some of them were reading, some were eating sandwiches and feeding crumbs to sparrows, and others were just resting, content in the miracle of spring.

The churchyard was the more peaceful and quiet, because of the noise in the background of cars and buses. It was like a ballet set and I expected any moment that somebody would get up and do a *pas seul* and then suddenly the whole place would be filled with dancing figures.

I went into the church. It was a Palladian affair in the eighteenth-century style, very light and gay with various marbles. There were three people in the church, the priest, the verger and a young man.

I knelt and pretended to pray. There was no one to pray to, but I felt terribly sorry for the priest. Out there in his churchyard there were a hundred people glorying in the sunshine; and inside only the young man and the verger, who was paid to be there, and me. I didn't count, because I was there on business. But for his sake I could pretend.

I thought, this was how Alex must have felt officiating in his empty chapel and the still emptier church in Dock Street, trying to console himself with, "Where two or three are gathered together in My name," while the heavy traffic thundered down to the docks.

It was twenty-seven years since I had heard the Order for Holy Communion. I had forgotten the beauty of its language. As the still familiar words came back to me, spoken bravely by the priest, it occurred to me that it might all be nonsense, but it was a *magnificent* waste of time and it did not matter if there were only one or two people in the congregation, provided that the churches were open. The very fact that in this busy city where at the moment almost everybody was engrossed in commerce, there was this priest celebrating the Lord's Supper to a legitimate congregation of one was magnificent.

At that moment the door of the church opened and a young woman, good-looking and well-dressed, but clearly worried about something, came in and knelt down to pray.

I found myself struggling with the Gloria, "Glory be to God on high, and in earth peace, good will towards men. We praise thee, we bless thee, we give thanks to thee for thy great glory, O Lord God, heavenly King, God the Father Almighty." It was merely an exercise in memory, how much one could remember after all those years.

"O Lord, the only-begotten Son Jesu Christ; O Lord God, Lamb of God, Son of the Father, that takest away the sins of the world, have mercy upon us . . ." I couldn't go on, even for the priest's sake. The idea of Jesus Christ taking away the sins of the world was impossible.

I looked at the girl, who seemed absolutely engrossed in her prayer. The priest raised his hands in benediction. "The peace of God which passeth all understanding, keep your hearts and minds in the knowledge and love of God, and of his Son Jesus Christ our Lord: and the blessing of God Almighty, the Father, the Son and the Holy Ghost, be amongst you and remain with you always."

That was no good for me. "But I hope it's some use to you," I thought, "because you're a jolly worried young woman."

I rang the Doctor's bell and as I waited I thought, "I suppose in an oblique way that was a form of prayer."

The door opened.

"Oh hallo, Miss Last!" I said.

"I'm Miss Langhorne," she answered. "Come in."

Dr Bullitt was out on an emergency call, a case of a boy with suspected appendicitis; but he came back soon, laughing.

"Just something he ate. Didn't tell his mother he'd eaten a pound of cooking apples."

Miss Langhorne brought tea, and the Doctor asked me what I made of Margaret. I had not sorted out my impressions, but I answered that I thought she was a very remarkable person.

"I'm worried about her," he said. "She doesn't seem to me to care any longer whether she lives or not."

He was of course right in a sense. She later told me that

it did not matter whether she lived or not. "After all if God takes me, I shan't be in any more pain and I shall be nearer to Him." It was a remark no novelist would dare to give one of his characters, because it would ring false. But spoken by someone with Margaret's belief and expectation of life, it was the simplest statement of fact. "We didn't discuss that," I said to Dr Bullitt. "But would it matter?"

"If the will to live goes . . ." The Doctor held out his hands hopelessly.

"Of course," I said. I did not want to take the conversation further, because we had reached an irreconcilable disagreement. A doctor must prolong life as long as it is possible. But if a human being has achieved his purpose, the time comes for the *Nunc Dimittis*. He is spiritually ready for death, as Stride told me Alex was at his end. Young though Margaret was, she had advanced spiritually further than almost anyone I had been privileged to meet. When she died, the loss would not be hers but that of those who knew her.

I changed the subject by saying how surprised I had been that the Padre had not disapproved of that old ruffian, the Admiral, whom we had met last night. "I had formed the idea of him as a rather disapproving man," I said. "I don't mean openly disapproving; but that, if I had met him, I should always have been checking myself, afraid that I might be treading on his corns."

The Doctor shook his head. "He was very strict with himself. But he never judged other people. I remember his saying to me once, 'B.P., how on earth can we blame young people for what they do? They have temptations the strength of which only God knows.'"

When we had finished tea, the Doctor took me to the big shelter, where he had worked in a casualty clearing station during the War.

As a film-set it was fantastic, a warehouse under the

vaulted arches of the old London, South Eastern and Chatham railway, about two hundred feet wide and nearly half a mile long. Half of it was heavily protected by a large office block but the rest merely gave an illusion of security. "It was very odd," the Doctor said. "I remember this place being used as an air-raid shelter during the First World War, when of course it was fairly safe, because the bombs were small. In the last war the Ministry of Home Security wouldn't schedule it as a shelter. But when the bombs started to drop, the group memory got to work and the people just occupied the place." He pointed to the bays on the west side, with raised platforms to facilitate the unloading of the railway trucks. "All those bays were filled with margarine. But it didn't make any difference. The people poured in and staked out squatting-rights on the top of the margarine. Fifteen thousand of them. Can you picture that? This whole place jammed with people. And knowing that if there was a direct hit there'd be a massacre, with probably as many casualties from the stampede as there would be from the bombing."

The place was absolutely empty, but I could fancy it as it must have been at that terrible time, though I myself was in the Army with an intake of riflemen drawn from this part of London. I remembered their anxiety during that superbly clear September of 1940, when we were drilling at Bushfield, just outside Winchester, with only an occasional machine-gunning while the Luftwaffe was concentrating on London. I remembered the calls the men tried to make from the telephone in camp and the money they lost because they hadn't learned to press Button B when they failed to get through. With two and ninepence a day I became a Button B pusher for my cigarettes. Not a proud memory. "There must have been epidemics," I said.

"There weren't," said Dr Bullitt. "In a way I was

more afraid of them than of the bombs. But there weren't. And by the time the bombs did fall, we'd got the population down . . . I've forgotten. Four or five thousand. The few bombs we had killed very few."

He sketched out the organization; where the canteen was, the casualty clearing station; the arrangement of the bays in sections with their leaders.

"And the Padre?" I asked. "What did he do?" I could see a dramatic film about a doctor in the blitz, but not about a priest.

"He wandered round," said the Doctor. "There were some people who wanted him to pray. But of course there was every religion here. They all knew who he was; that he'd been under fire; and because he was so calm, it was reassuring to the Jews and the Moslems and the rest."

I could understand that, and I could understand how with his particular belief he had a contagious courage. "But I can't understand what he thought he was doing by prayer," I said, "except perhaps getting people into the state of mind in which they didn't mind dying, if a bomb hit them. And it wouldn't matter much if they minded anyway. Didn't you ever ask him what he thought his prayers did? After all, he was a practical man from all accounts."

We walked down the long echoing vaults. "We were very busy in our different ways," said the B.P. "We didn't argue."

"But don't you see?" I said. "Don't you see that unless he was really doing something, when he prayed here, he was being . . . well a sort of holy ass?"

"He wasn't any sort of ass," said the Doctor.

"But how?" I asked, "how when a Nazi bomb-aimer is in a plane above London, aiming maybe at the docks or Tower Bridge, how does God ensure, just because the Padre says a prayer, that the bomb doesn't fall on this place?"

The Doctor laughed. "Don't ask me. I don't think about these things. I'm too busy with the tubercle and the spirochaete."

"How wise you are!" I said. "And yet I can't believe that Alex would have wasted all that time about nothing." As I said this, it occurred to me that perhaps the fact that no epidemic did occur and that the few bombs which did drop caused so few casualties might have been due to the Padre's prayers.

But equally of course it might not.

CHAPTER FIFTEEN

THE Padre had a small circle of parishioners to whom he gave nicknames and there was one of these, the Duchess, whom Father Williamson was emphatic I should meet. She was a remarkable character, he said, and she could tell me about when the bomb fell on Peabody Buildings.

I agreed the more willingly because I wanted some yardstick by which to judge my visit to the Earlers. Margaret was so obviously a special case that I was afraid I might be the victim of my own emotions. I did not wish to denigrate Alex's influence; but clearly his influence over a young woman whom he had known continuously since she was four or five years old would be more profound than his influence on someone who had already reached maturity, such as the Duchess.

Peabody Buildings consist of several blocks of tenements built to the west of Dock Street by a nineteenth-century philanthropist. Seeing them, I felt once again how unwise it was for a man to express his good intentions in bricks and mortar. The kindness of one century becomes the cruelty of the next. Peabody Buildings when they were new may have appeared splendid habitations for worthy Victorian workers, but today they seem sad, dark and grimly utilitarian.

The Duchess had two rooms on the ground floor of M Block. She kept them as neat and clean as it was possible for a woman crippled with what she called "screwmatics" or sometimes colloquially "the screws".

The Duchess was a woman in her seventies, a dowager

who held herself finely despite her pain. Her thin hair was strained back into a diminutive bun on the nape of her neck. Her nostrils arched thinly and it was easy to see the patrician qualities which earned her nickname. There was a strong smell of liniment, for which she apologized.

I had learned by now not to ask directly for information about the Padre. A person means something only in relation to our own lives and few can talk well of others without talking first of themselves.

The Duchess felt it due to herself to explain how she came to be in Peabody Buildings, which was the lowest rung in her descent of the social scale. I listened fascinated. Her flow was superb and her exposition of life could hardly have been better if she had been a professional lecturer. As a young woman she had married the manager of an off-licence in St John's Wood, close to Lord's Cricket Ground. Her husband had been a friend of Sir Pelham Warner, plain Plum Warner in those days, and they had spent pleasurable times wine-tasting. The firm was very satisfied with him. He was marked for promotion.

But then her husband fell ill, with a long wasting disease culminating in his death. She described the prime of her widowhood as a businesswoman, managing this and that establishment; and then the waning of her powers, until she had only the strength to look after old gentlemen.

After death had terminated several of her employers, she found her way to Peabody Buildings, where in these two rooms in M Block was living a widowed night-watchman, who needed looking after during the day.

The nightwatchman was a nice old man but the Duchess did not like Peabody Buildings. It was so gaunt and grim; and anyway living in a tenement was a come-down. She hovered and told him that there was another job, which she would like to enquire about before committing herself. This job sounded better. A retired major living in Bethnal Green wanted a companion. He lived in a house and not a tenement, and from outside it looked a nice place. But inside! The Major was lying on a bed standing on bare boards and the room reeked of the sweet stench of bugs.

The Duchess went back and told the nightwatchman, "There's worse places than Peabody Buildings. I'll do for you."

She never reckoned to live there. She came each day from her home in South London. But one night when the watchman was on duty, there was a terrible, terrible thunderstorm. The Duchess couldn't go back to where she lived, because of the long walk to the Underground and then the changes and the walk at the other end. So she popped into the nightwatchman's bed and next morning when he came back, there was a lovely breakfast waiting for him, porridge and two rashers of bacon and a fried egg and fried bread and hot toast. The nightwatchman rubbed his eyes in astonishment and then he smiled all over his face. "Oh my!" he said. "This is something."

When he had finished his breakfast, the nightwatchman lit his pipe and said he had an idea. Wasn't it silly the Duchess should go home every night, spending all that money in fares and rent and all, when she could easily sleep in the nightwatchman's bed and cook him breakfast when he came back from work? After all they were old enough not to bother what the neighbours said.

So they lived together as man and housekeeper, the nightwatchman sleeping in the bed during the day and the Duchess during the night, and of course it did save money.

Then someone said that the Duchess would be better off after the nightwatchman died if he married her. She would get more money as a pension and she could go on living in Peabody Buildings, M Block.

When the nightwatchman heard this, he said they

ought to get married; which they did quietly and no fuss.

They were both getting on and he was more and more frequently in hospital, because he had only one foot which gave him trouble. He was very popular in the ward, because he had a good voice. He sang from morning to night and they all loved that. But frequently she could not visit him, because she had the screws that bad. Then the Padre would act as go-between. He would go to the hospital and on his way home he would pop in and say, "Don't worry, Duchess. He was sitting up in bed, singing like a bird." He would gossip for a while and then he would say a little prayer and go away. Some people he gave things to, but not the Duchess. She didn't need charity but the prayer was nice.

But it wasn't as a clergyman they knew the Padre so much as a friend, especially in sickness. Only when the blitzes came, it was different.

I discovered from Father Weekes, who was the Vicar of St Paul's, Dock Street, at the time, that before the late War there was an agreement between him and the Padre, that Alex should confine himself to the Sailors' Home and sick-visiting, while Father Weekes devoted himself to the pastoral work of the parish. The emphasis was deliberately changed when Alex took over the shelter-visiting during the blitz.

For the Duchess, the most terrifying night of the blitzes was the Sunday in September 1940 when K Block was levelled by a land-mine.

Some of the rooms on the ground floor of M Block were bricked in and strengthened to provide shelter for the people in the block. It had been a terrible week-end, the warnings going almost immediately the All Clear was sounded. It had been one long Alert in a manner of speaking. The pubs were full of people, drinking heavily because they were frightened and excited.

On the Sunday evening the Alert went again. The barrage, which had been heavily reinforced, started up. It was deafening, but at intervals there was a lull and the droning of Nazi bombers could be heard, coming up the river. Many of the men ran out into the courtyard to look, but the women and children stayed in the shelter for the most part. The nightwatchman, who was not on duty, refused to go into the shelter. He sat in his easy chair, smoking his pipe. He said if there was a bomb with his number on it, that was that.

Suddenly the Duchess felt bad. The ceiling seemed to be pressing down. It was pressing down so hard that she felt it was going to crush her. She called out to the night-watchman, "It's falling! It's falling! Come into the shelter." But he went on sitting in his chair, smoking his pipe and reading the *News of the World* and he said, "You go. I'm staying here."

She ran out of the room but before she reached the shelter there was an explosion. It wasn't loud; not as loud as the guns, that is; sort of muffled. But the whole building shook and someone said, "Cor, that was a close one."

But even so they did not realize it was so close that it had fallen on K Block just across the street. When the land-mine exploded, the roof of K Block fell in and all the floors collapsed. Some of the people were sitting in their rooms, believing like the nightwatchman that they would not be killed unless their number was on a bomb. Most of these died instantly, though some lingered on, crushed by the masonry. But most of the people in K Block were in the shelters on the ground floor and they were buried alive.

Some of the men in M Block went out into the street and saw what had happened. They went back into the shelter and said, "Don't nobody go out." They did not say what had happened, but it was plain from their voices that it was something terrible which the children ought not to hear. So they asked no questions. But they all knew it was terrible, even the children, though they did not know exactly what it was.

For some time nobody spoke. They crowded into the dimly-lit shelter, listening to the thunder of the guns and the muffled thud of bombs exploding. Some of the children began to cry.

Then the Padre came in. He was wearing a tin helmet and he shone his torch round the shelter. "Are you all safe here?" he asked.

"Yes," they said, "we're all safe here, Padre."

It was a great relief to see anyone from outside, because the blitz was so violent that it seemed impossible to pass through it and live. Yet the Padre was as calm as calm. He lifted his right hand and blessed them, saying, "Peace be with you! In the name of the Father and of the Son and of the Holy Ghost."

As the Duchess told me this, she stood up, being for the moment the Padre as he had been, standing in the shelter. She was tremendously impressive as, with the mention of each Person of the Trinity, she made a cross in the air.

Then she broke off and said in her own voice: "I shall never forget that. He made us feel quite safe. He stayed a little while joking and then he went on. He had seen what had happened to K Block and he knew there were other people to comfort."

The Duchess's story was very dramatic. But neither that nor any of his other work during the blitz was very different from the work done by Father Groser and countless other priests down in the East End. Perhaps Alex had a special gaiety. But there was after all no one financially dependent on him. He was ready to die when his time came, and the Admiral side of him enjoyed the War. As an ex-Service man he took over the Sailors' Home the moment that War was declared.

The Duchess's story was certainly some use in explaining the place that he came to hold in the parish by the time of his death and the reason why so many came to his funeral, while so few had come to his services.

I saw this again a few days later at the dedication service of the window in the church. Father Williamson had hit on the happy idea of commemorating in this stained glass window both those killed during the late war and Alex who devoted his ministry to them. For a task of this sort he had not needed the help of any Captain Scrimgeoir. He had secured the Bishop of Stepney to dedicate the window and the Queen Mother to unveil it. The church was filled with people who had known Alex at different times in his career, a prodigious array of admirals, captains, commanders and lesser ranks, representatives of the Woods' family and civilian friends from every walk of life.

It was beautifully done. The church had been voluntarily re-decorated throughout inside and was fresh and clean and glorious. The Bishop preached a brief sermon on Alex which combined a practised fluency with earnest sincerity. Father Williamson apart from a hectic panic at the outset—"Royalty's early! Oh goodness me!"—controlled the service with great dignity. And the Queen Mother, looking radiant, was the most gracious of Majesties.

As she left the church, she was introduced to the specially privileged, such as General Woods and Dr Bullitt. I was in the back of the church and close enough to hear Williamson say, of the last in the row, a funny looking old lady with a deaf-aid, "And this is Lizzie Crouch, Ma'am. She's never missed a service in twenty-five years; she used to help the Padre in the chapel."

Lizzie Crouch was obviously one of the faithful, whom I had to see; but meanwhile, there were two receptions that could not be missed, a bun-fight for the "shipmates" at the Vicarage and a less august assembly at Dr Bullitt's.

The bun-fight was almost a dead loss. It merely confirmed my previous conviction that whatever significance Alex's naval career had in his total life remained a secret hidden from those with whom he served. They admired, loved and respected him, but they did not understand, or even consider there was any need to understand his development.

The person whom I was glad to meet was Hugh's daughter Valerie. I discussed with her the apparent indifference Alex felt to beautiful things, and she told me something which made me revise my judgment. When Alex was in hospital with pneumonia, she had taken him a bunch of flowers. She went back the next day, but brought no flowers, because he had some. She was very surprised to see that they had gone. "What had happened to them?" she asked.

"They were so beautiful that I had to give them away," he said. "One of the others fell in love with them and he had no flowers of his own."

The same instinct, she said, had led him at the beginning of the War, when he thought he might be killed, to give his nephews and nieces the money he would have left them as legacies.

Mrs Williamson said that he was by no means indifferent to beauty in people. She was once standing with him outside the church, and a girl nodded to her as she passed.

"Isn't she pretty?" Alex said. "Who is she?"

Mrs Williamson told him her name.

"Isn't that the girl we're praying for?" he asked.

She said it was.

"Oh then, I'll pray for her twice as hard," he said.

At Dr Bullitt's house I met first Mr and Mrs Canham. He had been keeper of the church schools in Well Close

Square and Alex had stayed with them before he moved in to the Sailors' Home. Mr Canham was a warden of St Paul's Church, an evangelical sort of man whose fate it was to get landed with one High Anglican after another. He didn't see eye to eye with the Padre on the ritualistic side, but it was a matter of pride that Mrs Canham and he were the only two witnesses when Alex was ordained priest by the Bishop of London in St Paul's Cathedral.

"What was he like?" I asked.

"He was a real gentleman," he said. "You always felt at ease with him. It didn't matter what you said or did. You felt at home with him. Different from Mr Weekes. You could never forget that Mr Weekes was a gentleman and you weren't. He made you unnatural."

When I repeated this criticism to Dr Bullitt later on, the Doctor agreed, with a qualification. "I think Canham imagined that Mr Weekes was doing that on purpose," he said, "to put him in his place. It wasn't that at all. He had a certain uneasiness of manner, which he felt as a great spiritual handicap and fought to overcome. But of course it was pointed by the Padre's exceptional case."

"Was there anything else which struck you about the Padre?" I asked Mr Canham.

"Well, of course the Padre thought the world of me," Mr Canham said. "Mrs Canham will confirm that."

"Oh yes," said Mrs Canham. "The Padre thought the world of Mr Canham."

A cynical part of me commented that perhaps the Padre's success with so many people, his ability as Badham said to make people feel at their best, was due to Alex's conveying to people that he thought the world of them. But then I corrected the emphasis. Alex was not self-conscious. He did not pretend to feelings which he did not have. He really did think the world of Mr Canham and the Duchess and the singing nightwatchman with one foot and Captain Scrimgeoir and even perhaps the red-biddy-drinking old Admiral. Was it due, I wondered, to some especial gusto, a delight in the human animal? Or was it part of the Christian duty of loving one's neighbour as oneself? I didn't see the sort of love which Alex had for people as being produced merely in the line of duty. It was a spontaneous love.

But how on earth could he have done it, when so many people are boring, commonplace or ignoble? The Christian ethic seemed to me to ask too much. No wonder so many Christians fell victims to hypocrisy.

That took me no further. Alex was not a hypocrite. He really did love his neighbour and yet he wasn't a fool. He did not close his eyes to weakness, vice or folly. There must be something in Christian doctrine to justify such love.

Of course, the doctrine of Redemption. If you really believed that Christ had died to save sinners, then every human being was not merely capable of achieving eternal life, but was already heir to eternity, even though he might not realize it. Supposing people did possess the sort of souls which Christianity posited, then every one of them became spiritually as precious to Alex as his patients were physically to Dr Bullitt. Granted the proposition that Jesus Christ was the Incarnate Son of God, everything else followed logically. But I could not swallow that proposition any more than could Leslie Coleman, to whom Dr Bullitt introduced me next.

Coleman had been a steward on a liner before he took over Chief Steward's job at the Sailors' Home. He was a little paunchy chap with a bright red face and shiny black curly hair, an excellent caterer and manager, as I found to my pleasure when I went to see him later at his pub in Bishops Stortford. He was a practical man, far more concerned with the problems of serving good wholesome meals with a low budget and second-rate staff than with saving souls. His aims had gone no further than the elimination of bugs from the old building. In this he had found the Padre an ally. The chapel was outside his scope. He was quite content to be a Martha-type, looking after the physical needs of the people in his charge.

He was a fighter, the sort who prefers to get his way after a bit of a scrap rather than by the exercise of diplomacy. He worked very well with the Padre, putting up his ideas in violent language which he knew Alex would suitably tone down for the committee, provided that he accepted them as sound. He resigned from the Sailors' Home on what he considered a matter of principle, but might partly have been injured pride. He considered that the architect should have consulted him about the new building. He believed that his experience of the difficulties of running the place with the sort of staff that could be obtained was of great value. "He may be a good architect," he said, "but he's never had to run a kitchen in a Sailors' Home. How can he overcome the snags till he knows what they are?"

His one anxiety in leaving the Sailors' Home was that the Padre might not be looked after properly. "I took Lewis the steward on one side—the one they call William —and I made him swear that he'd look after the Padre and never leave the home while Padre was alive," he said. "And I must say he did a wonderful job."

"You were devoted to the Padre?" I asked.

"There was nothing I wouldn't do for him."

"Did knowing the Padre cause you in any way to alter your religious beliefs?"

He looked surprised. "Of course not," he said. "I don't believe in all that stuff about the life hereafter. Hell's on earth and I think we ought to try and make a heaven of it."

So there I was back again. Margaret's faith could be

discounted. Her parents were religious anyway. But the other people whom he had known for years—Dr Bullitt, Badham, Coleman, the Duchess, the Canhams—they were devoted to him, but he had not altered their religious beliefs, converted them to Christianity if they were non-believers, or to his own High Anglicanism if they were already Christians. It puzzled me. Stride had tried to explain it by saying that he wasn't concerned with altering people's beliefs. He would not try to convert a Jew to Christianity. He would ask him if he had been to the Synagogue and say, "Good boy," if the answer was "Yes." He was quite happy for Methodists to go to chapel and Quakers to meeting-house. Was it, I wondered, a sort of doctrinal humility, the conviction only that his form of religion was right for himself.

The word humility recalled another conversation with Stride. He told me he had had an argument with the Padre, saying that he could not stomach the Christian regard for humility. "Humility," Alex had answered, "humility is to recognize what you can do and do it to the best of your ability." Did that not imply not attempting to do what you recognized that you could not do? Did Alex, with his "brain like Winnie the Pooh", consider that the intellectual conversion of others to Christianity was not one of the things he should even attempt to do?

I put the theory to Dr Bullitt. "I don't know of anybody he converted," he answered, "so I am as much in the dark as you are. But you must remember that you have only met a very small number of the thousands of people the Padre knew. As far as I could see, he concentrated on two sorts of people; the sick and the young. There must be some limitation of effort. He chose the sick because they might die, and he could help them to die in a state of grace. He chose the young because at the Sailors' Home there were a lot of boys going to sea for the first time, and if he could set them straight to start with there was a good chance they might keep straight. That's why he was so keen on training them in signalling—apart from the fact that he loved it—it gave him something technical in common with them. It is quite possible that the Padre did bring a number of those boys to church. The answer to that you will probably hear *after* the book is published. Those men are scattered all over the world, but some of them may write to you."

"I noticed you didn't use the word 'convert'," I said.

"Padre didn't like it," the Doctor answered. "Not in a violent sense. Violent conversions were too emotional. They didn't stick."

"What about the Road to Damascus?" I said.

The Doctor thought, his mouth twitching. "Wouldn't you call that visionary? By 'emotional' I was thinking of Saturday night on the Penitents' Bench."

CHAPTER SIXTEEN

Two days later I went back to the East End. My first visit was to Lizzie Crouch. I looked forward to it with some excitement. The moment I had seen her in the church I had felt that she was someone whom I had to see. It was more than a hunch. It was similar to the feeling I had when I saw the snapshot of Margaret Earler. The correct word to describe it was that Lizzie Crouch was in some way "designated" to help me.

She lived with her equally deaf sister in one of a row of mid-nineteenth-century cottages off Leman Street, the sort which in Chelsea are modernized throughout, given primrose or scarlet doors with the numbers painted on them in small italics and the window-sills made gay with petunias, but which in East London are scheduled for demolition and left standing for years without any repairs being done.

I banged the heavy old iron knocker on the door as hard as I could, and after a time Lizzie opened it and showed me into the front room. Her sister shouted down from the floor above to know if it was anyone for her. Lizzie shouted back No, it was for her and closed the door behind her.

Everything was very old and very clean. There was only one chair in the room. She insisted on my taking it and she sat on something made out of a packing-case. She was wearing a hat to receive me, as Alex's mother might have done in her day. "I want to help you," she said, "but I don't know what you want. He was a very good man." Her voice was very soft and gentle, the voice of a little girl rather than an old woman, yet inside it was quite hard; rather like a peach, the flesh and stone.

"I was his server," she said. "Not when anyone else was there. But when nobody came. I was against it. I said, 'It's not for a woman.' But he said, 'No, you've rung the bells and you've washed the church linen and you've collected the offertory; you can do this too.' So I did it and he was so very strict about the ablution, which I did at the end for him because his hands were so weak and it had to be just perfect. Is that the sort of thing you want to know?"

"Did you wash the linen?" I asked. "I didn't know that."

"I started in 1913," she said. "Mother was alive then and I washed the linen for the church. That's what I did. But when I tolled the bell I couldn't hear if it was ringing or not. But you don't want to know that." She sighed. "There's nothing really to say except that he loved God and God loved him. That's all there was to it."

"I want to know the little things," I said; "anything you remember."

"You saw the picture in the chapel," Lizzie said, "Peter trying to walk upon the waters?"

"I saw that."

"There was something wrong with St Peter's eye?"

"There certainly was."

"Someone shot him with an airgun. Right through the eye. The Padre was upset. Terribly. That anyone should want to do a thing like that. He had it patched and painted over, but it was never the same."

"Why should anyone want to shoot St Peter in the eye with an airgun?" I asked the question of myself as much as of Lizzie. Was he drunk? But why go in the chapel with an airgun? More like an air-pistol. Perhaps bought in a pub during the evening? A toy. Man comes back, maudlin. Wants to see Padre to talk about his soul. Goes to his cabin. No Padre there. Maybe in chapel. Goes across to see. No Padre there either. Damn. Never is Padre when wanted. Feels air-pistol. Takes it out. Lovely toy. Looks round and sees Peter walking on the water. Lovely picture, lovely target-picture. What the hell's the use of a Padre if he isn't there when wanted? Click goes the trigger. Pock goes the bullet. Got the sinking geezer right through the optic. Serve the old Padre right. God Almighty, what've I done? Better scapa. A possible explanation. I can't believe that sober people commit sacrilege.

"Why set fire to the altar?" Lizzie asked. "Someone done that; much about the same time it was. Thought it was a Pole they did. Never knew for sure." She paused, looking at me to see whether this was what I needed. "Somebody said it might be an accident."

"Did you think so?"

"It was on purpose. That's what the Padre knew too. That's why it hurt so."

"But why should anyone do it?" The sacrilege did not worry me. If God existed, He could not be anything but sorry for some miserable creature who had to vent his hatred and unhappiness in this way. It was Alex I was sorry for. The chapel was the visible sign of his love of God, and these were the altar-cloths made by his sister, the ones he had shown with such pride on H.M.S. *Greenwich*.

"Is this what you want me to tell you?" she asked again. "Some people hate God. But the Padre loved Him."

"Tell me more of when you worked with him," I said, "apart from the servings and the ablutions."

"Of course you know he couldn't celebrate Holy Communion. After he broke his femur. He couldn't stand up.

That made him very unhappy, because it was what he loved best, the celebration. And when Father Groser said it would be all right to celebrate sitting down, he was so happy. They made something for him at the home, so that it looked as if he was standing up, but he was sitting. And he celebrated and was happy again."

"He seems to have lived for Holy Communion," I said.

"Of course," she answered. "But right at the end he was so weak, he'd clutch my arm and say, 'Help me out, Lizzie, quick.' He was afraid he would fall in the chapel or faint."

She had prepared for my visit. She went to a corner and brought out all the things of his which she had kept. There was the little book he had given her on Lancelot Andrewes, his Bible, all the notes for sermons which she still had, and various other scraps. "Take anything that will help you," she said. "But please send them back. It's all I have left."

I took all, and perhaps more than, I needed. She had given me in what she said more than all the Admirals and the Captains and Commanders. She had a vividly factual mind of great honesty. "There is just one thing more," I said; "you've known many people who love God?"

"Yes," she said. "I've known quite a number, in my time."

"This is the question I want to know the answer to. Was the Padre different from the others? And if so, in what way was he different?"

For a moment she looked puzzled. Then she said, "Of course he wasn't different. Except he loved God more than most."

As I walked to the Sailors' Home, I realized that this was the question the failure to ask which had confused the whole of my research up to this point. I had been trying to write the biography of an individual, a personality, a character, somebody who was unique or exceptional. I had been foiled at every turn, because Alex in fact was merely an ordinary Christian, so stripped of any other qualities that he was either nothing, or a saint. Or to put it more precisely he was nothing but a saint, whereas St John of the Cross was a saint and a poet, St Thomas Aquinas was a saint and a theologian, St Joan of Arc was a saint and a soldier. I checked myself. Alex Woods was a saint and a signaller.

I felt thirsty and went into a pub. I bought a dry sherry and raising my glass, I said to myself, "God bless Lizzie Crouch!" The moment I had said it, I realized what a silly thing it was to say. God had already blessed her, if He existed; and the right thing would have been for her to ask Him to bless me.

As I walked down to the Sailors' Home for luncheon, I began to think out the implications of a Christian faith. Lizzie's account of the Padre struggling to administer Holy Communion with a broken femur was very gallant, but as I said to Stride, "If he had really believed, he should surely have recovered. There must have been a lapse of faith."

I waited for him to wriggle out of that one. But he was not caught. "That's just what I told him," he answered, "and he hearkened unto me. 'You're quite right, Boy Stride,' he said. He went along to Father Neville and received the sacraments of Anointment and the Laying on of Hands. There was a great improvement after that."

I knew that Father Neville was a member of the Anglican Order of Franciscans, who ran a coloured seamen's mission and hostel in Cable Street. He was one of the people whom I had to see, but I had postponed it because I had not been clear hitherto what I wanted to ask him.

"And what are the sacraments of Anointment and the

Laying on of Hands?" I asked. "How can they succeed where doctors fail?"

"It's a mystery which I don't pretend to understand," said Stride, "but perhaps Father Neville could tell you."

Before making an appointment with Father Neville, I called on the Earlers. There was the usual scene with the dog. But Mrs Earler was no longer cagey. She greeted me warmly, showed me up to Margaret's room and then excused herself to go down and quieten the dog.

I told Margaret what I had been doing, hoping that she might be able to give me helpful sidelights. She had heard of the shooting of St Peter and the burning of the altar, but she had nothing to add. But on the Laying on of Hands she became excited.

When the Padre had had the Sacrament of the Laying on of Hands, there had been two others who had received it, Margaret herself and a young West Indian. The West Indian had cancer of the liver. The hospital authorities had given up hope. In the doctors' opinion, his life was a matter of weeks, even days. That was over a year ago and the West Indian was still alive.

The Padre had been unable to walk except with the aid of sticks, before the Laying on of Hands. He so improved that at the end of his life he needed only one stick and moved with so much greater ease that he was talking of discarding that.

"And that was due to the Laying on of Hands?" I asked.

"What else could it have been?"

Dr Bullitt had given me a version, which made no mention of any Laying on of Hands. What he said was that after the femur was broken, a pinning operation was performed, which was unsuccessful. He went back for a second operation and this one succeeded.

Margaret was as ignorant of the second operation as

Dr Bullitt was of the Laying on of Hands. Both of them were vague about dates. There was nothing to be proved from the Padre's case.

It seemed to me one of the insuperable objections to the truth of the Bible was that miracles were recorded as performed not only by Jesus Christ but also by his disciples, which were unparalleled today—at least in my experience. If the Christian revelation is true, great faith should be as rewarded in the twentieth century A.D., as in the first. "What about you?"

"I am better," she said. "When I received the Laying on of Hands, I was still staining. They had to give up giving me streptomycin, because of its side-effects on me. Now I've had no staining for months now. I expect to be up soon."

I felt incredulous. "And what does Dr Bullitt say?"

"I'm not under him," she said. She gave me the name of a woman specialist at the Stepney Chest Clinic.

"You don't mind if I check with her?"

"Of course not," she said. "But there's one thing which Father Neville says. The point of the Laying on of Hands, and even more of the Anointment, is not cure, but resignation to God's will; to ask him to make one well, if that is what He wills, but to accept whatever happens, knowing that He will judge what is best. And that's what's happened. If God wants me to die, I'm not frightened. The next world anyway will be lovelier than this."

I did not argue. Even if she was mistaken in her expectation of a life after death, what strength it gave her in coping with the sorrows and sickness of this world. It was an enviable faith, even if it did not produce results as spectacular as those recorded by the evangelists. But there seemed to me a sort of double-think concealed in this doctrine of the Laying on of Hands; and for that matter in the Christian view of prayer. If God was all-powerful, all-knowing, all-wise and all-loving, His decisions must be for the best. Therefore to pray that He should alter those decisions was tantamount to a denial of His power, knowledge, wisdom and love. The prayer of request was really a form of blasphemy.

I checked with the woman specialist at the Chest Clinic. "I don't under-estimate the part that faith has played in Margaret's case," she said. "Her resistance in spite of the long-continued wasting is remarkable. Whatever her physical state, her cheerfulness is based on something more durable than any treatment we here can give." Margaret had been too ill to be taken to the X-ray department, but as far as the doctor could tell from the stethoscope, the lungs had healed. But it was not possible to say the extent to which this was due to antibiotics or to faith. Both, in the doctor's opinion, had played important parts. Even if the tuberculosis was completely arrested, the damage to lung-tissue was such that a total recovery was impossible. Activity which would be normal in a healthy person would place too great a strain on the heart.*

The next day I called on Father Neville at the Brown Brothers' poverty-stricken (or more accurately poverty-sanctified) headquarters in Cable Street. Margaret had described him as "more like the Padre than anybody I've ever known." He was pitifully thin, though whether through illness or the practice of austerity I do not know. Nor do I know whether he was growing a beard or just had not shaved for some time. I had the impression that he did not know either. It was not his concern.

I do not mean by this that he appeared "absent-minded". His mind and spirit were vividly alert, catching my inexpert queries, re-formulating them and giving the answers.

* Some months after this, Margaret contracted pleurisy, as a result of which the staining recurred. But this was not necessarily tubercular. The doctor's prognosis of heart trouble was confirmed.

"I have not practised the Laying on of Hands for very long," he said, "nor the sacrament of Anointment. I don't really know what happens. Perhaps one day I may understand. You must realize that both of these are sacraments. The Laying on of Hands is the simpler. In certain circumstances it can be done to someone who is not a Christian. Anointment cannot. Spiritual preparation is essential."

I questioned him about the relation between faith-healing and the medical treatment received by the people to whom he gave these sacraments. If he wanted to find out about the nature of faith-healing, it seemed to me that he would have to work in close collaboration with the doctors, checking a patient's response to a sacrament as carefully as a doctor would check responses to a drug. Unless medical treatment ceased altogether, while faith-treatment was given, it would be impossible to establish scientifically what was doing what to the patient.

Even as I was saying this, I realized what a chasm lay between us. The Franciscan was not interested in proving anything or in discovering what precise physical effects he was achieving. "To cure is the less important aim," he said. "The purpose of these sacraments is the attainment of a spiritual state, an acceptance of the Divine Will. The petition is made that the sick person may recover, if it is God's Will that he should recover. If no recovery is made, then the disease or death is accepted, because it is the Will of God."

I fumbled to convert this into terms of my own. "You mean that some illness may be caused, or prolonged, by what Christians call sin, or the psychologists an unconscious desire to escape into illness? The Laying on of Hands may get the thing psychologically right—ensure that the causatory sense of sin is removed—so if the disease persists, it is accepted as proof of the Divine Will instead of human frailty?"

He shrugged his shoulders. It was clear that he did not

mean this. There were ideas which could not be translated from his language to mine. Why waste time in trying? "Perhaps the object of an illness is to secure this resignation. If that happens, the purpose of the illness is achieved." He left it all a thought too light even to be a hypothesis. "The sacrament makes it easier to face the future," he said, "in whatever world."

But I was not satisfied. I wanted proof. Granted a faith-cure was a reward for faith, God's requital for absolute trust (which meant that it would be denied to anyone seeking scientific proof), wasn't it possible *afterwards* to determine what had happened, how much doctors had done and how much God? "What about the Padre? Would you attribute his recovery to the second operation or to the Laying on of Hands?"

Again he shrugged. (Perhaps I was striking at the root of his healing powers, trying to undermine faith with scientific curiosity?) "Does it matter?" he asked. "At the end he could walk."

I did not press it further. I was filled with a sense of spiritual inadequacy. What the Franciscan could teach me I was not ready to learn. It was like a schoolboy asking Einstein about relativity. "Is there anything else?" he asked.

He was very busy, but I did not want to leave him. "There's only one thing," I said. "What was he like, the Padre?"

He smiled and said nothing for almost a minute. I knew without his telling me that he could see Alex in his mind's eye as vividly as if he were standing in the room with us. Then he said, "He was the humblest man I have ever known. I was his confessor. To receive the confession of such a holy man . . . to see the standard which he set himself . . . it filled me with a sense of my unworthiness."

Hearing this admission from the lips of Father Neville,

a man so utterly devoted to his God, filled me with the sense of *my* unworthiness. I said good-bye, wanting as quickly as possible to be gone from a man every one of whose remarks came to me as a rebuke for cloddish intrusion where one should step delicately.

I stepped out on to the narrow pavement of Cable Street. A stream of heavy lorries from the east thundered past a foot away. Three Africans, who looked as if they had just come from the jungle, stood at the corner of the passage running down to Well Close Square. I turned down the passage. In the square it would be quiet. I could collect my thoughts there perhaps, as Alex had done when he wanted peace from the clamour of the Sailors' Home. (Or would he have gone into his chapel or a church?)

I had seen about all the people whom it would be profitable to see. Yet where had I got? It was like the pursuit of a phantom, or a figure in a dream. He would appear at a distance, apparently substantial. I would race towards him, but just as I was drawing close, he vanished. I was brought up short. And there he was, in another distance as inviting, and as evanescent on approach. I knew more about the facts of his whole life than anyone living. Yet I knew nothing. I had exposed a falsehood. I had charted the course from childhood onwards and arrived at what seemed plausible explanations of the moments of decision. Yet Alex remained as elusive as ever; not because he was a very complicated man, but because he was holy, a man of God.

I walked round and round the square, trying to think what other lines of approach there were. Among the papers which Lizzie Crouch had given me were notes on his sermons, which he had written out for her, because she could not hear well enough to follow by ear. I had read the sermons. They were interesting enough. By reading the biblical texts on which they were based, it was possible to arrive at what Alex had said. In one case he had gone into church with a choice of sermons. If the congregation consisted merely of "the faithful" he had a sermon based on the Witch of Endor about the dangers of spiritualism and the meaning of Ember Days. But if a stranger was present, he intended to drop this, because it was too specialized a subject, in favour of a sermon on the Gift of the Holy Spirit, based on the conclusion of the gospels of St Matthew and St Luke. I had learnt something from them. But it had not brought me to the heart of the matter.

Then I remembered a battered old notebook which Stride had handed to me with what I felt to be exaggerated reverence. "Here you are," he said. "This is the heart of the matter."

I opened it. "But this is just a list of names," I said. "There aren't even any addresses. And even if there were, I couldn't write to all these. There are too many."

Stride nodded, smiling. "There are over twelve hundred. Those he prayed for."

I stared at the meaningless lists with the headings of different days of the week; a weekly rota; about one hundred and seventy-five intercessions daily. "When they died, he didn't cross them out," I observed. "Just put a cross at the side and R.I.P."

"In Paradise they still needed his prayers," Stride said.

I had taken the notebook, because I did not want to hurt Stride's feelings; and it was impossible anyway just to dismiss outright what had occupied hours of the Padre's life every day. This was, in his view, the most important part of his work. What in fact had he been doing? And all these other Christians, did they really believe they could influence the material world by praying? The idea was utterly fantastic. But on the other hand, they were sensible, intelligent people. They wouldn't do it unless they had some impression that it was efficacious.

The trouble was that even Christians admitted that prayer was ineffectual, unless one had faith. How was I, without faith, to find out anything about it?

"Anyway," I thought, "there must be plenty of text-books on the Theory and Practice of Prayer. I can find out, at least, what Christians think they are doing when they pray."

CHAPTER SEVENTEEN

I HAD reached the point which I had foreseen when I had undertaken to write the life of Alex, but which I had refused to anticipate. How could I, an agnostic, understand a man whose love of other men and women sprang from his love of the God in whom I would have liked, but was unable, to believe? How could I, without any religious experience, penetrate the secrets of a man who spent a large part of his life in meditation, intercession and the contemplation of God?

It seemed a task as impossible as it would have been for me to write about some scientific subject for which I had no qualification, such as relativity or the quantum theory.

Yet it was surprising, as I had found when writing documentary films, how easy it was, faced with some entirely strange field of knowledge or activity, to gain a working knowledge of it. I decided to try approaching Prayer in rather the same way. It must have a theory and practice.

The Vicar of Cranleigh gave me two small books, one by himself, the other *The School of Prayer* by Olive Wyon, saying that if these did not help, he would find something else. Olive Wyon had a chapter on Prayer and the Purpose of God, which dealt in some detail with intercession.

"Does she suggest how it works?" I asked.

"I am afraid that none of us knows *how* prayer works," he answered, smiling. "But I can assure you that it *does* work."

That was fair enough; at the end of every corridor of knowledge, however long, we come to a locked door behind which is what we must accept as existing but not understood.

I went home and read the chapter on Prayer and the Purpose of God. I could not understand it, though it was clear that the author was writing with care and precision of a spiritual activity, very hard to describe in words because it took place beyond words. "The first step in intercession," I read, "is to make a definite 'act' of union with this stream of God's love and power, which is flowing ceaselessly out of His Heart and back to Him again." It meant something, but I could not understand what it meant, because it described no experience which I had ever had.

I copied out certain passages on my typewriter in the vague hope that writing it down, having it on sheets of paper belonging to me, would make it more intelligible. "The greatest works wrought by prayer have been accomplished, not by human effort but by human trust in God's effort. In prayer of this kind we are united with the very life of God, sharing in His Work . . ."

It was exciting to think that there were many different kinds of prayer. I had the crude idea that Christians believed that prayers must be spoken, or at least thought in words; and that posture was important; that God must be approached, meekly and very uncomfortably, kneeling upon your knees.

If God existed, it seemed to me, prayers of request for oneself or even for others came in the lower grades. The first instinct was to adore. "We praise Thee, we bless Thee, we worship Thee, we glorify Thee, we give thanks to Thee for Thy great glory." In the Communion Service it was an outpouring. But soon words would become a barrier between the worshipper and God. There, as far as I had seen, the worship ended. The good rains seeped away in the sand and one was left in the desert.

But Dr Wyon wrote of a wordless contemplation, "a quiet 'dry' prayer," one of whose temptations, she said, "is to feel that we 'are doing nothing'; in a sense this is true, for our main work is to let God work through us. Yet in another sense, we are being very active, only our concentration is so intense that we seem to be standing still."

I would not have been so certain that Dr Wyon was writing of some spiritual activity, which though I had never experienced it was absolutely authentic, if I had not seen its outer expression in Father Neville and the other Christians I had met during the last few months. This was the heart of the matter, as Stride had said. This was the secret of Alex, which was in fact no secret but the common experience of all who had "seen" God.

This realization made things no easier for me. It emphasized the sense of being outcast in a shadowed land and the brilliance of the country on the other side of the chasm. I had an impulse to say some prayer, asking God for help. It took every effort of my will to resist it. To say a prayer would be a form of cheating. I sat at my desk, looking out over the garden, not-praying as hard as I could. I had control over my speech, but within me I felt the gathering of an irresistible longing to be given what would make this quiet, dry prayer of contemplation possible.

I have to use words to say what happened next, though translation into words falsifies something which was ineffable. I had the sensation of being lifted up in spirit and carried from the shadowed country across the chasm into the light. I made no effort of any sort, either to further or to resist this translation of the spirit. I was in someone else's hands.

This happened many months ago, and in the meantime

I have thought a lot about what happened that morning. I believe the clue is to be found in what Dr Wyon says of intercession.

"The third sign of divine activity towards man is that deep *effort* suggested by the mysterious words of St Paul about the 'groanings of the Spirit which cannot be uttered . . .' There are two ways in which this effort can be made by us; one is by system (making lists, remembering certain people and causes on certain days and the like); the other is by simply holding up the person we desire to help and placing him or her, as it were, in the current of the flowing stream of the love and power of God."

We tend to think only of the active side of intercession, what the intercessor does. But when it succeeds, there is also a passive side, what happens to the intercessee. The only explanation I can find of this translation, which took place contrary to my will, is that someone interceded with God, whose love was stronger than my unfaith.

I have speculated who that person was. It may have been any one of the Christians to whom I had talked about Alex. Father Neville, for example, to whom I had talked only the day before, must have worried that Alex's life was being written by someone obviously so ill-equipped to understand him. It might have been his intercession, or that of half a dozen others.

I believe, for reasons which I shall give later, that my intercessor was Alex, who had been following the course of this book with love and sympathy, to say nothing of the amusement of literally "ghosting" his biography, keeping himself always in the background and leading me to the love of God, which was his secret.

Whatever the explanation, I found myself, after the lapse of what time I don't know, still sitting at my desk, looking out of the window, but with the conviction that I had been given faith. It seemed most improbable. I did not believe in such things happening to anybody, least of all to myself. My feeling of joy was tempered by the fear that at any moment I would wake up.

If it was true, on the other hand, it would mean that the gospels would no longer appear implausible. It was possible that I had been given faith in God, but not in Jesus Christ. I decided to read the Gospel according to St Luke, treating it not as a work of piety but as if the postman had just delivered an advance copy of it for review.

In the past it had always defeated me, because I had tried to separate the bits I could accept from the miraculous parts which I rejected on materialist grounds. Once one started in this way, it was astonishing how little one could accept. The miracles came so thick and fast.

This time I read St Luke assuming that God existed, which meant that if He chose, He could suspend natural laws. These natural laws themselves were after all so miraculous and the created universe so compelling of wonder that the operation of supernatural laws to supersede them on occasion was quite conceivable. In consequence I applied the criterion, "If Jesus Christ was the Son of God, would things have happened this way?"

It seemed to me they would. The story of Jesus belonged not to the order of myth, but to the order of history. The only two episodes in the Gospels which did not seem consistent with Christ's being the Son of God were the Gadarene swine and the cursing of the barren fig-tree. The rest magnificently cohered, with the gradual dawning of the realization that Jesus was not just a very holy man, or the Messiah as conceived by the Jews, but actually God Incarnate. It was astonishing. It was almost incredible. But it was more credible than any of the attempts to explain the gospels as mixtures of historical truth and mythical accretions, or Jesus as an actual man to whom attributes of Divinity had been added.

243

I felt very bewildered, not merely by this change of belief but also because it was not accompanied by any of the things which I thought should accompany it. I felt no sense of sin or of repentance; only a great joy and the desire to worship God in his every manifestation, in the appearance of Creation and the spirit moving within, in God the Creator of the Universe who yet could love the least of His creatures, in God eternal yet ever close, God to be worshipped and loved not just on Sundays in church on one's knees, but everywhere in any posture or at any minute of waking life.

It was not a conversion in the Penitents' Bench sense, though it was in the sense used to translate the Greek Metanœa, a change in the way of thinking. Nor was it as sudden as it appeared to me at the moment of receiving faith. That sharply-defined moment of change was the end of what I can now see as a groping search extending over years and rapidly accelerated during my research into the life of Alex.

That research I had temporarily to abandon; or rather I had to turn for the moment from Alex himself to the contemplation of God, Whose love was the climate in which Alex flourished. That I was granted such a vivid and constant sense of God's nearness was due not to any merit but to the fact that for me to understand the selfless quality of the Padre's devotion I had to feel the warmth and brilliance of God's love. I had to be taught that in giving his life to God, Alex was receiving it again even more abundantly; that that physical suffering for which I had pitied Alex became by the alchemy of Christianity a love-offering to the Christ crucified; that these prayers of request which I had thought of a low order as much gratified God the Father to grant, if in our true interest, as it gratifies a human father to give his children what they ask for, if it is not harmful. I had to learn that what I had thought of as the Christian doctrine that we should love

244

our enemies, was not a doctrine but a statement of fact. Hatred of our enemies cuts us off from the love of God. The love of God makes us love our enemies.

In learning these things for myself, I was at the same time learning them about Alex. It was the logical continuation of the search which had begun with asking those he loved to tell me about Alex. It was God he loved best.

When I turned my mind again to the book, it seemed to me plain that what had been intended all the time was not a straight biography of the Admiral of the sort which he would have hated, but something along the lines of what I have written. I could imagine a scene in Paradise, when the old Jutland lie was revived in the obituary notice. I could imagine God saying, "What are we going to do about this, Alex?" and Alex answering, "Let's forget it, Lord. It'll die a natural death."

Then perhaps God said, "No, you've loved me very well. And I know you'll hate this, but I think a book about you might help other people."

"If you say so, Lord," Alex would reply, obedient but embarrassed. "But will you at least let me manage it my way." And typically his way was to step out of the limelight and leave it shining on the love of God.

I do not mean this in an irreverent or a whimsical way. When I started to rewrite the book, something very strange happened, which gave a new meaning to its title, *No Earthly Command*. Normally I start working in the morning at about ten o'clock and work off and on until ten or eleven in the evening. I then go to bed and sleep heavily until half-past six or seven the next morning.

The first thing that happened was that I stopped sleeping soundly. I woke to an immediate watchfulness, coming from the depths of sleep to an instant sense of the nearness of God. This happened at increasingly frequent intervals. It was only once a night to start with, then

245

twice, then every hour just before the clock struck the hour downstairs, then half-hourly.

The next thing that happened was that I was told to go downstairs and work. Sometimes it was six o'clock, more usually between half-past four and half-past five. This continued for the whole duration of the second draft of the book, a matter of ten weeks. I have never in my life had so little sleep over such a long period. Yet there was absolutely no sense of undue fatigue. I would be tired when I went to bed, but when I woke up an hour later I was quite fresh.

It was a strange experience, but from what von Hügel wrote in *The Meaning of Prayer*, it seems a common one.

> [St Bernard] bids his monks rise never so early for the night choir prayer in the coldest midwinter; they will find God awake, Him the awakener; they will find Him waiting for them, always anticipating even their earliest watches.

In the same little book I found the warning which supported me when the draft was finished. Contemplation, he said, might become a sort of spiritual intoxication. It might appear to be effortless, but it had a "neural cost". How true this was, I discovered on Monday morning at half-past seven, when after two hours work the draft was finished. I was exhausted.

It would have been nice to discover that a book written under such sustained compulsion had a special quality. But unfortunately it hadn't. I had written too fast, or not fast enough. I had not given time for the Metanoēsis, the change of mind. By the time the comments of all the interested parties had come in, my understanding of what had happened had so changed that the book had to be re-written.

CHAPTER EIGHTEEN

SOME saints understand sin because they have sinned themselves. They have explored continents of illusion in search of the satisfactions which they find to perfection only in God. Because they travelled a long circuit before they found what they needed, they can help others who have become disillusioned about the possibility of finding anything except what they are disillusioned with.

Alex was not that sort of saint. He seems to have been unassailed by doubts and never to have greatly sinned. In forms and beliefs his religion was completely orthodox. But it was never conventional. He worshipped as he did, not because his Church told him to, but because God did. The conclusions which he reached were the same conclusions which millions of other Christians had reached; but he received them from God. If God had told him something else, he would have obeyed unflinchingly.

There were two sorts of hypocrite, he said. There was the old-fashioned sort, who pretended to be better than he was; and the new-fashioned sort, who pretended to be worse. He was neither sort. That is why though he was always a good man, he was never a prig or goody-goody.

He saw life from the grandstand of innocence. But what he saw he understood. He was the most chaste of men, but he understood the forms of lechery. He drank very little, but he was the friend and saviour of drunkards. He hated evil, but he loved people, even those who thought themselves evil or were thought evil by others.

He was delivered from the wastes of theological controversy by his lack of intellectual curiosity. He read his Bible with intelligence and care, and from it he supplemented what he received direct from God. He was not a complex man; his character was all of a piece. He loved God and his neighbour as himself. But as one can see from the Gospels, obedience to those two commandments demands greater spiritual subtlety than disobedience. He was not a clever or a sophisticated man. But he had wisdom and what St Paul's translators call "ghostly strength". This wisdom came to him in part from prayer and study of the Bible and in part from sympathy with others. I have said that he had little personal experience of sin and vice, but he learned from the sins and vices of others the tolerance which most people gain only through their own transgression.

When he was at the Sailors' Home he was always available. Boy Stride had a problem and needed advice. Leslie Coleman had the solution of a problem and needed help to get it across. Sailors, ships' cooks, apprentices and would-be signallers drifted in and out, wanting help or comfort or money. He combined this availability with an intense devotional life, I imagine carrying with him on bus and train journeys that old notebook with the lists of those for whom he interceded. Because God was always so close, he could switch from an intercession to helping a drunk to bed and back to intercession without great difficulty. His whole life was a prayer, which took many different forms, from baptizing new-born babies to praying for the dead.

I think that the reason why I heard so little of Alex converting anyone to religion was because he did not think that was the right approach for him. He distrusted the idea of talking or arguing people into religious belief; though he would probably have agreed that some people find discussion and argument stimulating and helpful. It was not for him. He had the humility to concentrate on doing what he could do to the best of his ability. His weapon was not dialectic but prayer. Rather than plead with someone, he preferred to intercede for them. He considered that God could help others far more than he could.

This does not mean that he did not use his influence to bring others into the Church. During the War sailors would come into his cabin, just before they were leaving. Ostensibly they had come to say good-bye, but they usually said, "Don't forget to say a prayer for us, Padre."

That gave him the chance to ask if they belonged to any church denomination. If he found that they hadn't been baptized and confirmed, he pointed out that these were sacraments ordained by God, and He would be better pleased if they took them before they sailed.

The man would probably have the double objection, that he had no time and (less easy to avow) that baptism was something done to babies, and confirmation to kids when their voices broke. Alex overcame them both by an arrangement with the Bishop of Stepney, whereby men wanting baptism or confirmation could receive it privately and, if going to sea, without the usual preparation.

But this was, I think, not an attempt to lead a man to God. It was opening the way for the man himself to find Him, the sacraments doing more than any amount of argument.

Yet this did not mean that he relied on God to do for him the material things which were his duty. When a West Indian living opposite the Sailors' Home appealed to the Padre, because he and the nine other West Indians living in the room next door to the water-closet couldn't get in or out without getting their feet foul from the overflow, Vice-Admiral Woods was on to the slum-landlord threatening him with the visitation of the sanitary inspector unless the lavatory was repaired immediately. He was by conviction a Tory, but at the end of the War he voted for Labour because he thought his beloved merchant seamen would get a better deal from them; though at the next election he reverted to Tory, because he thought Labour had failed.

His behaviour was so unobtrusive that it is best exemplified by a mistake. The Beloved Physician told me that in all the years he knew him the Padre never called him in on his own behalf, though he summoned him hundreds of times for others. It was always left for someone like Stride to call the Doctor if the Padre was ill; and four or five times in those years he was ill with pneumonia.

One of these occasions was in 1944, when London was being heavily bombarded with flying bombs. As soon as the Doctor saw the Padre, he called an ambulance and the Padre was taken to the Seamen's Hospital, Greenwich, where under a course of M and B he was soon out of danger.

The Doctor was very busy. The flying bombs were causing many casualties and there was no time for him to go to Greenwich to see the Padre personally, though he telephoned the hospital every day to find out how the patient was progressing.

It was over a week before the Doctor found time to go to Greenwich. When he went into the ward, the Padre said, "Thank God, B.P. It's wonderful to see you."

The Doctor took this to imply a reproach that he had not been to see him earlier and he was very surprised, because it was so uncharacteristic. The Padre was the first to visit those who were sick and the last to expect that he should be visited.

Hours later what the Padre had meant came to him. It was not that he had wanted a visit, but that he had been afraid that the Doctor might be killed or wounded by a flying bomb.

The progressive muscular atrophy slowly wasted certain of his leg and hand muscles. But he behaved as though there was no disability and unobservant people noticed none. When Dr Hierons was investigating the disease, however, Alex offered to visit the hospital if ever the Doctor wished to demonstrate what the symptoms looked like.

It was only after he fell in his room and broke his femur that he was really crippled. He could not move without the irons which reached from the foot to the thigh. Some people said he ought to retire. But where should he retire to? All his brothers were older than he; Hugh, the youngest and more able-bodied of them, was no age to turn male nurse.

It was far best that he should stay at the Sailors' Home. There he had the devoted attention of William, the steward, who took off his irons as he lay on the bed and put them on for him before he rose in the morning. He had the love and companionship of his friends in the club and the parish. Though less active he could still move about and still pursue the spiritual tasks of his ministry.

As the shadow of death crept towards him, everybody became more and more conscious that this unobtrusive Admiral turned Padre was somebody very special. Though it was not a word which they often used or gave any precise meaning to, they began to say that the Padre was a saint.

During the War a legend had grown round him, about his courage and humour under fire, his love of God and men and women and children, and especially of sailors. Now to this legend was added the conviction that this frail old man was closer to God than anyone they would ever meet in this lifetime. He became a sort of human talisman. While he was alive, God was in that place.

In October 1955, he contracted pneumonia again and was taken to the Sailors' Hospital, Greenwich. He responded to treatment, but was very tired. What people noticed, however, were his gaiety and his radiance. His grasp of affairs stayed firm. Visitors read his letters to him and he followed the news they gave him keenly. He even asked after the welfare of Dr Bullitt's cats. When Stride came, he wanted to know what Badham had done for the sailors out of work.

"Don't worry!" Stride said. "They're all placed, every one of them."

"Not Jones!" Alex said. "Jones, as near a half-wit as made no difference, was the first to fire and last to hire."

"Yes. Even Jones."

"Good, Boy Stride."

The Bishop of Stepney went to see him. When Alex opened his eyes, he said, "Who are you?"

"I'm your Bishop."

"Oh, help!" said Alex.

Lettice and Dr Bullitt went to see him and he said to Lettice. "You know, my child, don't you believe it when people tell you that when you're on your death-bed, you think only of repentance. It's not true. For the last four days I haven't thought of any such thing; in fact, haven't thought of any spiritual matters at all."

"You've nothing to repent for," she said, "and you're not dying."

He smiled. "I've made my confessions for the sins I've committed." And he told her a story he'd read of three boys in a Cathedral, one of whom was "dared" to make confession. The Priest saw through him and told him to go to the High Altar and look at the crucifix and say, "This is what you have done for me and I don't care a fig for Thee." The Bishop who told him the story said, "I know it's true, because I was the boy."

On Thursday, 28 October, he received Holy Unction and Communion from Father Williamson and Communion again on the Sunday, and on the Monday, All Saints' Day, he died at peace with all worlds.

EPILOGUE

I SAID in Chapter Seventeen that I believed it was the intercession of Alex which enabled me to cross the chasm, and that in the development of the book I detected the quality of his mind with its love, humour and unobtrusiveness.

Throughout the book I have pointed out the strange mixture of coincidences and improbabilities which led to that frail misbegotten obituary notice becoming a hardcover book of an entirely different sort from what any of the human beings involved projected. I have also pointed out how the initial resistance to the idea gave way to co-operation, in many cases without any communication from me. With the only person I really tried to win over, the Admiral who was one of Alex's closest friends in the Navy, I failed. The people with whom I succeeded were all conscious of Alex, not as a person who was green in their memories, but as a presence who was close to them. In each case they said they had concluded that Alex, though hating the idea, would have agreed if he felt it would further God's purpose.

A conspicuous thing in the research was the timing. Father Williamson forgot to tell Boston and myself that the Jutland story was a lie at the moment when that revelation would have strangled the idea at birth. Lettice assumed that I must have been told. The lie was not revealed until I was on the brink of meeting Margaret Earler.

Dr Bullitt agreed to help at the moment when I was

trying to decide whether to do the book. I wrote and suggested our meeting. Months passed while I worked on the early part of the book. Then the time came when I decided that next day I would telephone the Doctor. There was no need, because there was a letter in the post that morning.

The same thing happened with the Admiralty. I was terrified that their permission to consult documents would come while I was sorting out my ideas in the Metanoësis. I had information that permission had been granted a week before. The day after I had sorted things out, the letter came.

I wrote to Phyllis Sealey in Cheshire, saying I wanted to see her. She was coming to a village a few miles away in a week's time.

Perhaps it was all chance, but I came to rely on it. Someone or something was managing this business far more smoothly than I could myself. I was curiously without worry.

So when I finished the chapter describing Alex's death, I felt that it was inconclusive. Alex had somehow had a hand in this affair from the other side. But the question was, how? I had not thought about the question of life after death. God's succour on earth had been enough to content me. But there surely must be some Christian teaching which might explain what had been happening.

The next day I received a letter from Phyllis Sealey, saying, "Alex has been much in my mind recently, so I am wondering if that means you have been progressing with his 'Life'? Quite a month ago I wrote to Mr Williamson to ask for two copies of Alex's *Why we should pray for the Dead*, to send to you and Hugh—but he never replied, so I hope this means the leaflets were sent direct."

I had received no leaflet and I could see no use to which I could put it anyway, so I wrote back, "Is there any very

254

particular reason why I ought to read *Why should we pray for the Dead*?"

That night I was woken up in the sharp way I have described. There was one thought in my mind. "That letter was not coincidence. Alex wants me to read it." Then I realized that it was what he had written when he was alive about the state after death. If he wanted me to read it, this must be in answer to my wonder about the role he might have played.

I wrote asking for the leaflet and it arrived by return, a little duplicated sheet called *Let Light Perpetual Shine upon Them, or Why We should Pray for the Dead*. In it Alex said that after death the soul was in an intermediate state or phase, before it reached its final destination, Paradise, Hades or the Hell of the Creed (as opposed to the Hell of Punishment).

In this state, he said, those who for one reason or another had no experience of Christ in their early lives were given a second chance. They were helped in this by the intercession of the living, who could also have communion with spirits of just men being made perfect.

> Truly penitent faith and confession of sin gains for us free pardon. But the fact that we are forgiven does not immediately alter our Character. We believe that such reformation is completed in the intermediate state in which souls are made perfect and ready to enter Heaven.

This deepened my understanding of Alex's faith. The Church Militant here on Earth, the Church Expectant in Paradise, and the Church Triumphant in Heaven, were one and the same Church. But the reason, it seemed to me, why I had been sent the leaflet was contained in another sentence.

> It is in that process of "being made perfect" that they are helped by our prayers and that *when they have been made perfect, they can help us*.*

* My italics.

This was what Alex had been doing for me, for those whom I met and I am sure for hundreds of others whom I have not met. In Paradise or in Eternity it is impossible that he would forget the sailors whom, when he was on earth, he defended in public, lauded in private and interceded for with God.